THE
BOOK OF CATS

THE
BOOK OF CATS

edited by

GEORGE MACBETH

and

MARTIN BOOTH

William Morrow and Co., Inc.

New York

Contents

IV Cat's Love

V Cat's Magic

VI Cat's Killings

IX Cat's Resurrection

Cat, *n.* A soft, indestructible automaton provided by nature to be kicked when things go wrong in the domestic circle.

This is a dog,
    This is a cat,
This is a frog,
    This is a rat.
Run, dog, mew, cat,
Jump, frog, gnaw, rat.
        Elevenson (Ambrose Bierce)

I

Cat's Youth

How the Cat Became

Ted Hughes

Things were running very smoothly and most of the creatures were highly pleased with themselves. Lion was already famous. Even the little shrews and moles and spiders were pretty well known.

But among all these busy creatures there was one who seemed to be getting nowhere. It was Cat.

Cat was a real oddity. The others didn't know what to make of him at all.

He lived in a hollow tree in the wood. Every night, when the rest of the creatures were sound asleep, he retired to the depths of his tree—then such sounds, such screechings, yowlings, wailings! The bats that slept upside-down all day long in the hollows of the tree branches awoke with a start and fled with their wing-tips stuffed into their ears. It seemed to them that Cat was having the worst nightmares ever—ten at a time.

But no. Cat was tuning his violin.

If only you could have seen him! Curled in the warm smooth hollow of his tree, gazing up through the hole at the top of the trunk, smiling at the stars, winking at the moon—his violin tucked under his chin. Ah, Cat was a happy one.

And all night long he sat there composing his tunes.

Now the creatures didn't like this at all. They saw no use in his music, it made no food, it built no nest, it didn't even keep him warm. And the way Cat lounged around all day, sleeping in the sun, was just more than they could stand.

"He's a bad example," said Beaver, "he never does a stroke of work! What if our children think they can live as idly as he does?"

"It's time," said Weasel, "that Cat had a job like everybody else in the world."

So the creatures of the wood formed a Committee to persuade Cat to take a job.

Jay, Magpie, and Parrot went along at dawn and sat in the topmost twigs of Cat's old tree. As soon as Cat poked his head out, they all began together, "You've to get a job. Get a job! Get a job!"

That was only the beginning of it. All day long, everywhere he went, those birds were at him, "Get a job! Get a job!"

And try as he would, Cat could not get a wink of sleep.

That night he went back to his tree early. He was far too tired to practise on his violin and fell fast asleep in a few minutes. Next morning, when he poked his head out of the tree at first light, the three birds of the Committee were there again, loud as ever, "Get a job!"

Cat ducked back down into his tree and began to think. He wasn't going to start grubbing around in the wet woods all day, as they wanted him to. Oh no. He wouldn't have any time to play his violin if he did that. There was only one thing to do and he did it.

[3]

He tucked his violin under his arm and suddenly jumped out at the top of the tree and set off through the woods at a run. Behind him, shouting and calling, came Jay, Magpie, and Parrot.

Other creatures that were about their daily work in the undergrowth looked up when Cat ran past. No one had ever seen Cat run before.

"Cat's up to something," they called to each other. "Maybe he's going to get a job at last."

Deer, Wild Boar, Bear, Ferret, Mongoose, Porcupine, and a cloud of birds set off after Cat to see where he was going.

After a great deal of running they came to the edge of the forest. There they stopped. As they peered through the leaves they looked sideways at each other and trembled. Ahead of them, across an open field covered with haycocks, was Man's farm.

Harleian manuscript (*British Library, London*)

But Cat wasn't afraid. He went straight on, over the field, and up to Man's door. He raised his paw and banged as hard as he could in the middle of the door.

Man was so surprised to see Cat that at first he just stood, eyes wide, mouth open. No creature ever dared to come on to his fields, let alone knock at his door, Cat spoke first.

"I've come for a job," he said.

"A job?" asked Man, hardly able to believe his ears.

"Work," said Cat. "I want to earn my living."

Man looked him up and down, then saw his long claws.

"You look as if you'd make a fine rat-catcher," said Man.

Cat was surprised to hear that. He wondered what it was about him that made him look like a rat-catcher. Still, he wasn't going to miss the chance of a job. So he stuck out his chest and said, "Been doing it for years."

"Well then, I've a job for you," said Man. "My farm's swarming with rats and mice. They're in my haystacks, they're in my corn sacks, and they're all over the pantry."

So before Cat knew where he was, he had been signed on as a Rat-and-Mouse-Catcher. His pay was milk, and meat, and a place at the fireside. He slept all day and worked all night.

At first he had a terrible time. The rats pulled his tail, the mice nipped his ears. They climbed on to rafters above him and dropped down—thump! on to him in the dark. They teased the life out of him.

But Cat was a quick learner. At the end of the week he could lay out a dozen rats and twice as many mice within half an hour. If he'd gone on laying them out all night there would pretty soon have been none left, and Cat would have been out of a job. So he just caught a few each night—in the first ten minutes or so. Then he retired into the barn and played his violin till morning. This was just the job he had been looking for.

Man was delighted with him. And Mrs Man thought he was beautiful. She took him on to her lap and stroked him for hours on end. What a life! thought Cat. If only those silly creatures in the dripping wet woods could see him now!

Well, when the other farmers saw what a fine rat-and-mouse-catcher Cat was, they all wanted cats too. Soon there were so many cats that our Cat decided to form a string band. Oh yes, they were all great violinists. Every night, after making one pile of rats and another of mice, each cat left his farm and was away over the fields to a little dark spinney.

Then what tunes! All night long . . .

Pretty soon lady cats began to arrive. Now, every night, instead of just music, there was dancing too. And what dances! If only you could have crept up there and peeped into the glade from behind a tree and seen the cats dancing—the glossy furred ladies and the tomcats, some pearly grey, some ginger red, and all with wonderful green flashing eyes. Up and down the glade, with the music flying out all over the night.

At dawn they hung their violins in the larch trees, dashed back to the farms, and pretended they had been working all night among the rats and mice. They lapped their milk hungrily, stretched out at the fireside, and fell asleep with smiles on their faces.

[5]

The Kitten's Eclogue

Ruth Pitter

Auctor

Tell now, good kit, of three months' age, or less,
Whence dost thou bring thy perfect blessedness?
Beast which must perish, and all black to view,
What makes the happiness of such as you?

Bogy Baby

My sable hue, like Ethiopian queen,
My raven tincture and my jetty dye,
Not as defect or blemish can be seen
By anybody that hath half an eye.
What sight more welcome than the night above?
What hue more honoured in the courts of love?

Unseen at night I ramble, being black,
And against black you will not hear me rail.
They kept the sooty whelp for fortune's sake
When all my stripy brethren plumbed the pail.
Their mice I kill, I stuff me with their tuck,
And no man kicks me lest he spoil his luck.

The sex, which some a sorry burthen deem,
I glory in, and mightily rejoice;
Though but a babe, before the fire I dream
Already that I hear my lover's voice;
What music shall I have—what dying wails—
The seldom female in a world of males!

And when love's star above the chimneys shines,
And in my heart I feel the sacred fire,
Upon the ridge-tile will I hymn these lines
With which great Venus doth my soul inspire;
Then see the toms, in gallant cavalcade,
Come flying to the lovesick fair one's aid!

Black Cat, photo John Elliot (*Tourist Photo Library*)

What mortal dame, what merely human she,
What strong enchantress, could thus honoured sit;
What maid could draw her suitors on like me,
Sing such a tune and get away with it?
What charmer could men's souls so nearly touch?
What nymph, I ask, could do one half as much?

Hold me not foul for that I wanton be.
These amorous frolics are but innocence;
I court no fickle immortality,
And fear no judgment when I go from hence:
No hope, no dread my little grave contains,
Nor anything beside my scant remains!

BOGY BABY'S EMBLEM. O felis semper felix!
EVERYBODY ELSE'S EMBLEM. MUD.

[7]

The Cat that Walked by Himself

Rudyard Kipling

Hear and attend and listen; for this befell and behappened and became and was, O my Best Beloved, when the Tame animals were wild. The Dog was wild, and the Horse was wild, and the Cow was wild, and the Sheep was wild, and the Pig was wild—as wild as wild could be— and they walked in the Wet Wild Woods by their wild lones. But the wildest of all the wild animals was the Cat. He walked by himself, and all places were alike to him.

Of course the Man was wild too. He was dreadfully wild. He didn't even begin to be tame till he met the Woman, and she told him that she did not like living in his wild ways. She picked out a nice dry Cave, instead of a heap of wet leaves, to lie down in; and she strewed clean sand on the floor; and she lit a nice fire of wood at the back of the Cave; and she hung a dried wild-horse skin, tail-down, across the opening of the Cave; and she said, "Wipe your feet, dear, when you come in, and now we'll keep house."

That night, Best Beloved, they ate wild sheep roasted on the hot stones, and flavoured with wild garlic and wild pepper; and wild duck stuffed with wild rice and wild fenugreek and wild coriander; and marrow-bones of wild oxen; and wild cherries, and wild grenadillas. Then the Man went to sleep in front of the fire ever so happy; but the Woman sat up, combing her hair. She took the bone of the shoulder of mutton—the big flat blade-bone—and she looked at the wonderful marks on it, and she threw more wood on the fire, and she made a Magic. She made the First Singing Magic in the world.

Out of the Wet Wild Woods all the wild animals gathered together where they could see the light of the fire a long way off, and they wondered what it meant.

Then Wild Horse stamped with his wild foot and said, "O my Friends and O my Enemies, why have the Man and the Woman made that great light in that great Cave, and what harm will it do us?"

Wild Dog lifted up his wild nose and smelled the smell of the roast mutton, and said, "I will go up and see and look, and say; for I think it is good. Cat, come with me."

"Nenni!" said the Cat. "I am the Cat who walks by himself, and all places are alike to me. I will not come."

"Then we can never be friends again," said Wild Dog, and he trotted off to the Cave. But when he had gone a little way the Cat said to himself, "All places are alike to me. Why should I not go too and see and look and come away at my own liking?" So he slipped after Wild Dog softly, very softly, and hid himself where he could hear everything.

When Wild Dog reached the mouth of the Cave he lifted up the dried horse-skin with his nose and sniffed the beautiful smell of the roast mutton, and the Woman, looking at the blade-bone, heard him, and laughed, and said, "Here comes the first. Wild Thing out of the Wild Woods, what do you want?"

Wild Dog said, "O my Enemy and Wife of my Enemy, what is this that smells so good in the Wild Woods?"

Then the Woman picked up a roasted mutton-bone and threw it to Wild Dog and said, "Wild Thing out of the Wild Woods, taste and try." Wild Dog gnawed the bone, and it was more delicious than anything he had ever tasted, and he said, "O my Enemy and Wife of my Enemy, give me another."

The Woman said, "Wild Thing out of the Wild Woods, help my Man to hunt through the day and guard this Cave at night, and I will give you as many roast bones as you need."

"Ah!" said the Cat, listening. "This is a very wise Woman, but she is not so wise as I am."

Wild Dog crawled into the Cave and laid his head on the Woman's lap, and said, "O my Friend and Wife of my Friend, I will help your Man to hunt through the day, and at night I will guard your Cave."

"Ah!" said the Cat, listening. "That is a very foolish Dog." And he went back through the Wet Wild Woods waving his wild tail, and walking by his wild lone. But he never told anybody.

When the Man waked up he said, "What is Wild Dog doing here?" And the Woman said, "His name is not Wild Dog any more, but the First Friend, because he will be our friend for always and always and always. Take him with you when you go hunting."

Next night the Woman cut great green armfuls of fresh grass from the water-meadows, and dried it before the fire, so that it smelt like new-mown hay, and she sat at the mouth of the Cave and plaited a halter out of horse-hide, and she looked at the shoulder-of-mutton bone—at the big broad blade-bone—and she made a Magic. She made the Second Singing Magic in the world.

Out of the Wild Woods all the wild animals wondered what had happened to Wild Dog, and at last Wild Horse stamped with his foot and said, "I will go and see and say why Wild Dog has not returned. Cat, come with me."

"Nenni!" said the Cat. "I am the Cat who walks by himself, and all places are alike to me. I will not come." But all the same he followed Wild Horse softly, very softly, and hid himself where he could hear everything.

When the Woman heard Wild Horse tripping and stumbling on his long mane, she laughed and said, "Here comes the second. Wild Thing out of the Wild Woods, what do you want?"

Wild Horse said, "O my Enemy and Wife of my Enemy, where is Wild Dog?"

The Woman laughed, and picked up the blade-bone and looked at it, and said, "Wild Thing out of the Wild Woods, you did not come here for Wild Dog, but for the sake of this good grass."

And Wild Horse, tripping and stumbling on his long mane, said, "That is true; give it me to eat."

The Woman said, "Wild Thing out of the Wild Woods, bend your wild head and wear what I give you, and you shall eat the wonderful grass three times a day."

"Ah!" said the Cat, listening. "This is a clever Woman, but she is not so clever as I am."

Wild Horse bent his wild head, and the Woman slipped the plaited-hide halter over it, and Wild Horse breathed on the Woman's feet and said, "O my Mistress, and Wife of my Master, I will be your servant for the sake of the wonderful grass."

"Ah!" said the Cat, listening. "That is a very foolish Horse." And he went back through the

Man and Dog Hunting, 1822

Wet Wild Woods, waving his wild tail and walking by his wild lone. But he never told anybody.

When the Man and the Dog came back from hunting, the Man said, "What is Wild Horse doing here?" And the Woman said, "His name is not Wild Horse any more, but the First Servant, because he will carry us from place to place for always and always and always. Ride on his back when you go hunting."

Next day, holding her wild head high that her wild horns should not catch in the wild trees, Wild Cow came up to the Cave, and the Cat followed, and hid himself just the same as before; and everything happened just the same as before; and the Cat said the same things as before; and when Wild Cow had promised to give her milk to the Woman every day in exchange for the wonderful grass, the Cat went back through the Wet Wild Woods waving his wild tail and walking by his wild lone, just the same as before. But he never told anybody. And when the Man and the Horse and the Dog came home from hunting and asked the same questions same as before, the Woman said, "Her name is not Wild Cow any more, but the Giver of Good Food. She will give us the warm white milk for always and always and always, and I will take care of her while you and the First Friend and the First Servant go hunting."

Next day the Cat waited to see if any other Wild Thing would go up to the Cave, but no one moved in the Wet Wild Woods, so the Cat walked there by himself; and he saw the Woman milking the Cow, and he saw the light of the fire in the Cave, and he smelt the smell of the warm white milk.

Cat said, "O my Enemy and Wife of my Enemy, where did Wild Cow go?"

The Woman laughed and said, "Wild Thing out of the Wild Woods, go back to the Woods again, for I have braided up my hair, and I have put away the magic blade-bone and we have no more need of either friends or servants in our Cave."

Cat, Gwen John (*Tate Gallery, London*)

Cat said, "I am not a friend, and I am not a servant. I am the Cat who walks by himself, and I wish to come into your Cave."

Woman said, "Then why did you not come with First Friend on the first night?"

Cat grew very angry and said, "Has Wild Dog told tales of me?"

Then the Woman laughed and said, "You are the Cat who walks by himself, and all places are alike to you. You are neither a friend nor a servant. You have said it yourself. Go away and walk by yourself in all places alike."

Then Cat pretended to be sorry and said, "Must I never come into the Cave? Must I never sit by the warm fire? Must I never drink the warm white milk? You are very wise and very beautiful. You should not be cruel even to a Cat."

Woman said, "I knew I was wise, but I did not know I was beautiful. So I will make a bargain with you. If ever I say one word in your praise, you may come into the Cave."

"And if you say two words in my praise?" said the Cat.

"I never shall," said the Woman, "but if I say two words in your praise, you may sit by the fire in the Cave."

"And if you say three words?" said the Cat.

"I never shall," said the Woman, "but if I say three words in your praise, you may drink the warm white milk three times a day for always and always and always."

Then the Cat arched his back and said, "Now let the Curtain at the mouth of the Cave, and the Fire at the back of the Cave, and the Milk-pots that stand beside the Fire, remember what my Enemy and the Wife of my Enemy has said." And he went away through the Wet Wild Woods waving his wild tail and walking by his wild lone.

That night when the Man and the Horse and the Dog came home from hunting, the Woman did not tell them of the bargain that she had made with the Cat, because she was afraid that they might not like it.

Cat went far and far away and hid himself in the Wet Wild Woods by his wild lone for a long time till the Woman forgot all about him. Only the Bat—the little upside-down Bat—that hung inside the Cave knew where Cat hid; and every evening Bat would fly to Cat with news of what was happening.

One evening Bat said, "There is a Baby in the Cave. He is new and pink and fat and small, and the Woman is very fond of him."

"Ah," said the Cat, listening. "But what is the Baby fond of?"

"He is fond of things that are soft and tickle," said the Bat. "He is fond of warm things to hold in his arms when he goes to sleep. He is fond of being played with. He is fond of all those things."

"Ah," said the Cat, listening. "Then my time has come."

Next night Cat walked through the Wet Wild Woods and hid very near the Cave till morning-time, and Man and Dog and Horse went hunting. The Woman was busy cooking that morning, and the Baby cried and interrupted. So she carried him outside the Cave and gave him a handful of pebbles to play with. But still the Baby cried.

Then the Cat put out his paddy paw and patted the Baby on the cheek, and it cooed; and the Cat rubbed against its fat knees and tickled it under its fat chin with his tail. And the Baby laughed; and the Woman heard him and smiled.

Then the Bat—the little upside-down Bat—that hung in the mouth of the Cave said, "O my Hostess and Wife of my Host and Mother of my Host's Son, a Wild Thing from the Wild Woods is most beautifully playing with your Baby."

"A blessing on that Wild Thing whoever he may be," said the Woman, straightening her back, "for I was a busy woman this morning and he has done me a service."

That very minute and second, Best Beloved, the dried horse-skin Curtain that was stretched tail-down at the mouth of the Cave fell down—*woosh!*—because it remembered the bargain she had made with the Cat; and when the Woman went to pick it up—lo and behold!—the Cat was sitting quite comfy inside the Cave.

"O my Enemy and Wife of my Enemy and Mother of my Enemy," said the Cat, "it is I: for you have spoken a word in my praise, and now I can sit within the Cave for always and always and always. But still I am the Cat who walks by himself, and all places are alike to me."

The Woman was very angry, and shut her lips tight and took up her spinning-wheel and began to spin.

But the Baby cried because the Cat had gone away, and the Woman could not hush it, for it struggled and kicked and grew black in the face.

"O my Enemy and Wife of my Enemy and Mother of my Enemy," said the Cat, "take a strand of the thread that you are spinning and tie it to your spindle-whorl and drag it along the floor, and I will show you a Magic that shall make your Baby laugh as loudly as he is now crying."

"I will do so," said the Woman, "because I am at my wits' end; but I will not thank you for it."

She tied the thread to the little clay spindle-whorl and drew it across the floor, and the Cat ran after it and patted it with his paws and rolled head over heels, and tossed it backward over his shoulder and chased it between his hind legs and pretended to lose it, and pounced down upon it again, till the Baby laughed as loudly as it had been crying, and scrambled after the Cat and frolicked all over the Cave till it grew tired and settled down to sleep with the Cat in its arms.

"Now," said Cat, "I will sing the Baby a song that shall keep him asleep for an hour." And he began to purr, loud and low, low and loud, till the Baby fell fast asleep. The Woman smiled as she looked down upon the two of them, and said, "That was wonderfully done. No question but you are very clever, O Cat."

That very minute and second, Best Beloved, the smoke of the Fire at the back of the Cave came down in clouds from the roof—*puff!*—because it remembered the bargain she had made with the Cat; and when it had cleared away—lo and behold!—the Cat was sitting quite comfy close to the fire.

"O my Enemy and Wife of my Enemy and Mother of my Enemy," said the Cat, "it is I: for you have spoken a second word in my praise, and now I can sit by the warm fire at the back of the Cave for always and always and always. But still I am the Cat who walks by himself, and all places are alike to me."

Then the Woman was very very angry, and let down her hair and put more wood on the fire and brought out the broad blade-bone of the shoulder of mutton and began to make a Magic that should prevent her from saying a third word in praise of the Cat. It was not a Singing Magic, Best Beloved, it was a Still Magic; and by and by the Cave grew so still that little wee-wee mouse crept out of a corner and ran across the floor.

"O my Enemy and Wife of my Enemy and Mother of my Enemy," said the Cat, "is that little mouse part of your Magic?"

"Ouh! Chee! No indeed!" said the Woman, and she dropped the blade-bone and jumped upon the footstool in front of the fire and braided up her hair very quick for fear that the mouse should run up it.

"Ah," said the Cat, watching. "Then the mouse will do me no harm if I eat it?"

"No," said the Woman, braiding up her hair, "eat it quickly and I will ever be grateful to you."

Cat made one jump and caught the little mouse, and the Woman said, "A hundred thanks. Even the First Friend is not quick enough to catch little mice as you have done. You must be very wise."

That very minute and second, O Best Beloved, the Milk-pot that stood by the fire cracked in two pieces—*ffft!*—because it remembered the bargain she had made with the Cat; and when the Woman jumped down from the footstool—lo and behold!—the Cat was lapping up the warm white milk that lay in one of the broken pieces.

"O my Enemy and Wife of my Enemy and Mother of my Enemy," said the Cat, "it is I: for you have spoken three words in my praise, and now I can drink the warm white milk three times a day for always and always and always. But *still* I am the Cat who walks by himself, and all places are alike to me."

Then the Woman laughed and set the Cat a bowl of the warm white milk and said, "O Cat, you are as clever as a man, but remember that your bargain was not made with the Man or the Dog, and I do not know what they will do when they come home."

"What is that to me?" said the Cat. "If I have my place in the Cave by the fire and my warm white milk three times a day I do not care what the Man or the Dog can do."

That evening when the Man and the Dog came into the Cave, the Woman told them all the story of the bargain, while the Cat sat by the fire and smiled. Then the Man said, "Yes, but he has not made a bargain with *me* or with all proper Men after me." Then he took off his two leather boots and he took up his little stone axe (that makes three) and he fetched a piece of wood and a hatchet (that is five altogether), and he set them out in a row and he said, "Now we will make *our* bargain. If you do not catch mice when you are in the Cave for always and always and always, I will throw these five things at you whenever I see you, and so shall all proper Men do after me."

"Ah!" said the Woman, listening. "This is a very clever Cat, but he is not so clever as my Man."

The Cat counted the five things (and they looked very knobby) and he said, "I will catch mice when I am in the Cave for always and always and always; but *still* I am the Cat who walks by himself, and all places are alike to me."

"Not when I am near," said the Man. "If you had not said that last I would have put all these things away for always and always and always; but now I am going to throw my two boots and my little stone axe (that makes three) at you whenever I meet you. And so shall all proper Men do after me!"

Then the Dog said, "Wait a minute. He has not made a bargain with *me* or with all proper Dogs after me." And he showed his teeth and said, "If you are not kind to the Baby while I am in the Cave for always and always and always, I will hunt you till I catch you, and when I catch you I will bite you. And so shall all proper Dogs do after me."

"Ah!" said the Woman, listening. "This is a very clever Cat, but he is not so clever as the Dog."

Cat counted the Dog's teeth (and they looked very pointed) and he said, "I will be kind to the Baby while I am in the Cave, as long as he does not pull my tail too hard, for always and always and always. But *still* I am the Cat who walks by himself, and all places are alike to me."

"Not when I am near," said the Dog. "If you had not said that last I would have shut my mouth for always and always and always; but *now* I am going to hunt you up a tree whenever I meet you. And so shall all proper Dogs do after me."

Then the Man threw his two boots and his little stone axe (that makes three) at the Cat, and the Cat ran out of the Cave and the Dog chased him up a tree; and from that day to this, Best Beloved, three proper Men out of five will always throw things at a Cat whenever they meet him, and all proper Dogs will chase him up a tree. But the Cat keeps his side of the bargain too. He will kill mice, and he will be kind to Babies when he is in the house, just as long as they do not pull his tail too hard. But when he has done that, and between times, and when the moon gets up and night comes, he is the Cat that walks by himself, and all places are alike to him. Then he goes out to the Wet Wild Woods or up the Wet Wild Trees or on the Wet Wild Roofs, waving his wild tail and walking by his wild lone.

Midwife Cat

Mark Van Doren

Beyond the fence she hesitates,
  And drops a paw, and tries the dust.
It is a clearing, but she waits
  No longer minute than she must.

Though a dozen foes may dart
  From out the grass, she crouches by,
Then runs to where the silos start
  To heave their shadows far and high.

Here she folds herself and sleeps;
  But in a moment she has put
The dreams aside; and now she creeps
  Across the open, foot by foot,

Till at the threshold of a shed
  She smells the water and the corn
Where a sow is on her bed
  And little pigs are being born.

Silently she leaps, and walks
  All night upon a narrow rafter,
Whence at intervals she talks
  Wise to them she watches after.

II

 Cat's Meat

Milk for the Cat

Harold Monro

When the tea is brought at five o'clock,
And all the neat curtains are drawn with care,
The little black cat with bright green eyes
Is suddenly purring there.

At first she pretends, having nothing to do,
She has come in merely to blink by the grate,
But though tea may be late or the milk may be sour,
She is never late.

And presently her agate eyes
Take a soft large milky haze,
And her independent casual glance
Becomes a stiff, hard gaze.

Then she stamps her claws or lifts her ears
Or twists her tail and begins to stir,
Till suddenly all her lithe body becomes
One breathing, trembling purr.

The children eat and wriggle and laugh;
The two old ladies stroke their silk:
But the cat is grown small and thin with desire,
Transformed to a creeping lust for milk.

The white saucer like some full moon descends
At last from the cloud of the table above;
She sighs and dreams and thrills and glows,
Transfigured with love.

She nestles over the shining rim,
Buries her chin in the creamy sea;
Her tail hangs loose; each drowsy paw
Is doubled under each bending knee.

A long dim ecstasy holds her life;
Her world is an infinite shapeless white,
Till her tongue has curled the last holy drop
Then she sinks back into the night,

Draws and dips her body to heap
Her sleepy nerves in the great arm-chair,
Lies defeated and buried deep
Three or four hours unconscious there.

The Cat's Dinner, Marguerite Gérard (*Musée Fragonard, Grasse*)

War Cat

Dorothy L. Sayers

I am sorry, my little cat, I am sorry—
if I had it, you should have it;
but there is a war on.

No, there are no table-scraps;
there was only an omelette
made from dehydrated eggs,
and baked apples to follow,
and we finished it all.
The butcher has no lights,
the fishmonger has no cod's heads—
there is nothing for you
but cat-biscuit
and those remnants of yesterday's ham;
you must do your best with it.

Round and pathetic eyes,
baby mouth opened in a reproachful cry,
how can I explain to you?
I know, I know:
"Mistress, it is not nice;
the ham is very salt
and the cat-biscuit very dull,
I sniffed at it, and the smell was not enticing.
Do you not love me any more?
Mistress, I do my best for the war-effort;
I killed four mice last week,
yesterday I caught a young stoat.
You stroked and praised me,
you called me a clever cat.
What have I done to offend you?
I am industrious, I earn my keep;
I am not like the parrot, who sits there
using bad language and devouring

parrot-seed at eight-and-sixpence a pound
without working for it.
If you will not pay me my wages
there is no justice;
if you have ceased to love me
there is no charity.

"See, now, I rub myself against your legs
to express my devotion,
which is not altered by any unkindness.
My little heart is contracted
because your goodwill is withdrawn from me;
my ribs are rubbing together
for lack of food,
but indeed I cannot eat this—
my soul revolts at the sight of it.
I have tried, believe me,
but it was like ashes in my mouth.
If your favour is departed
and your bowels of compassion are shut up,
then all that is left me
is to sit in a draught on the stone floor and look miserable
till I die of starvation
and a broken heart."

Cat with the innocent face,
what can I say?
Everything is very hard on everybody.
If you were a little Greek cat,
or a little Polish cat,
there would be nothing for you at all,
not even cat-food:
indeed, you would be lucky
if you were not eaten yourself.
Think if you were a little Russian cat
prowling among the cinders of a deserted city!
Consider that pains and labour
and the valour of merchant-seamen and fishermen
have gone even to the making of this biscuit
which smells so unappetising.
Alas! there is no language
in which I can tell you these things.

Well, well!
If you will not be comforted
we will put the contents of your saucer
into the chicken-bowl—there!

Harriet Martineau with her Cat, Alfred Croquis

all gone! nasty old cat-food—
The hens, I dare say,
will be grateful for it.

Wait only a little
and I will go to the butcher
and see if by any chance
he can produce some fragments of the insides of something.

Only stop crying
and staring in that unbearable manner—
as soon as I have put on my hat
we will try to do something about it.

My hat is on,
I have put on my shoes,
I have taken my shopping basket—
What are you doing on the table?

The chicken-bowl is licked clean;
there is nothing left in it at all.
Cat,
hell-cat, Hitler-cat, human,
all-too-human cat,
cat corrupt, infected,
instinct with original sin,
cat of a fallen and perverse creation,

The Cat's Meat Man, W. J. Webb

hypocrite with the innocent and limpid eyes—
is nothing desirable
till somebody else desires it?

Is anything and everything attractive
so long as it is got by stealing?
Furtive and squalid cat,
green glance, squinted over a cringing shoulder,
streaking hurriedly out of the back door
in expectation of judgment,
your manners and morals are perfectly abhorrent to me,
you dirty little thief and liar.

Nevertheless,
although you have made a fool of me,
yet, bearing in mind your pretty wheedling ways
(not to mention the four mice and the immature stoat),
and having put on my hat to go to the butcher's,
I may as well go.

Five Eyes

Walter de la Mare

In Hans' old mill his three black cats
Watch the bins for thieving rats.
Whisker and claw, they crouch in the night,
Their five eyes smouldering green and bright:
Squeaks from the flour-stacks, squeaks from where
The cold wind stirs on the empty stair,
Squeaking and scampering everywhere.
Then down they pounce, now in, now out,
At whisking tail, and sniffing snout;
While lean old Hans he snores away
Till peep of light at break of day;
Then up he climbs to his creaking mill.
Out come his cats all grey with meal—
Jekkel, and Jessup, and one-eyed Jill.

The
Story of Webster

P. G. Wodehouse

"Cats are not dogs!"

There is only one place where you can hear good things like that thrown off quite casually in the general run of conversation, and that is the bar parlour of the *Angler's Rest*. It was there, as we sat grouped about the fire, that a thoughtful Pint of Bitter had made the statement just recorded.

Although the talk up to this point had been dealing with Einstein's Theory of Relativity, we readily adjusted our minds to cope with the new topic. Regular attendance at the nightly sessions over which Mr Mulliner presides with such unfailing dignity and geniality tends to produce mental nimbleness. In our little circle I have known an argument on the Final Destination of the Soul to change inside forty seconds into one concerning the best method of preserving the juiciness of bacon fat.

"Cats," proceeded the Pint of Bitter, "are selfish. A man waits on a cat hand and foot for weeks, humouring its lightest whim, and then it goes and leaves him flat because it has found a place down the road where the fish is more frequent."

"What I've got against cats," said a Lemon Sour, speaking feelingly, as one brooding on a private grievance, "is their unreliability. They lack candour and are not square shooters. You get your cat and you call him Thomas or George, as the case may be. So far, so good. Then one morning you wake up and find six kittens in the hat-box and you have to re-open the whole matter, approaching it from an entirely different angle."

"If you want to know what's the trouble with cats," said a red-faced man with glassy eyes, who had been rapping on the table for his fourth whisky, "they've got no tact. That's what's the trouble with them. I remember a friend of mine had a cat. Made quite a pet of that cat, he did. And what occurred? What was the outcome? One night he came home rather late and was feeling for the keyhole with his corkscrew; and, believe me or not, his cat selected that precise moment to jump on the back of his neck out of a tree. No tact."

Mr Mulliner shook his head.

"I grant you all this," he said, "but still, in my opinion, you have not got to the root of the matter. The real objection to the great majority of cats is their insufferable air of superiority. Cats, as a class, have never completely got over the snootiness caused by the fact that in Ancient Egypt they were worshipped as gods. This makes them too prone to set themselves up as critics and censors of the frail and erring human beings whose lot they share. They stare rebukingly. They view with concern. And on a sensitive man this often has the worst effects, inducing an inferiority complex of the gravest kind. It is odd that the conversation should have taken this turn," said Mr Mulliner, sipping his hot Scotch and lemon, "for I was thinking only this afternoon of the rather strange case of my cousin Edward's son, Lancelot."

"I knew a cat—" began a Small Bass.

My cousin Edward's son, Lancelot (said Mr Mulliner) was, at the time of which I speak, a comely youth of some twenty-five summers. Orphaned at an early age, he had been brought up in the home of his Uncle Theodore, the saintly Dean of Bolsover; and it was a great shock to that good man when Lancelot, on attaining his majority, wrote from London to inform him that he had taken a studio in Bott Street, Chelsea, and proposed to remain in the metropolis and become an artist.

The Dean's opinion of artists was low. As a prominent member of the Bolsover Watch Committee, it had recently been his distasteful duty to be present at a private showing of the super-super-film, *Palettes of Passion*; and he replied to his nephew's communication with a vibrant letter in which he emphasised the grievous pain it gave him to think that one of his flesh and blood should deliberately be embarking on a career which must inevitably lead sooner or later to the painting of Russian princesses lying on divans in the semi-nude with their arms round tame jaguars. He urged Lancelot to return and become a curate while there was yet time.

But Lancelot was firm. He deplored the rift between himself and a relative whom he had always respected; but he was dashed if he meant to go back to an environment where his individuality had been stifled and his soul confined in chains. And for four years there was silence between uncle and nephew.

During these years Lancelot had made progress in his chosen profession. At the time at which this story opens, his prospects seemed bright. He was painting the portrait of Brenda, only daughter of Mr and Mrs B. B. Carberry-Pirbright, of 11 Maxton Square, South Kensington, which meant thirty pounds in his sock on delivery. He had learned to cook eggs and bacon. He had practically mastered the ukulele. And, in addition, he was engaged to be married to a fearless young vers libre poetess of the name of Gladys Bingley, better known as The Sweet Singer of Garbidge Mews, Fulham—a charming girl who looked like a pen-wiper.

It seemed to Lancelot that life was very full and beautiful. He lived joyously in the present, giving no thought to the past.

But how true it is that the past is inextricably mixed up with the present and that we can never tell when it may spring some delayed bomb beneath our feet. One afternoon, as he sat making a few small alterations in the portrait of Brenda Carberry-Pirbright, his fiancée entered.

He had been expecting her to call, for today she was going off for a three weeks' holiday to the South of France, and she had promised to look in on her way to the station. He laid down his brush and gazed at her with a yearning affection, thinking for the thousandth time how he worshipped every spot of ink on her nose. Standing there in the doorway with her bobbed hair sticking out in every direction like a golliwog's, she made a picture that seemed to speak to his very depths.

"Hullo, Reptile!" he said lovingly.

"What ho, Worm!" said Gladys, maidenly devotion shining through the monocle which she wore in her left eye. "I can stay just half an hour."

"Oh, well, half an hour soon passes," said Lancelot. "What's that you've got there?"

"A letter, ass. What did you think it was?"

"Where did you get it?"

"I found the postman outside."

Lancelot took the envelope from her and examined it.

[27]

"Gosh!" he said.

"What's the matter?"

"It's from my Uncle Theodore."

"I didn't know you had an Uncle Theodore."

"Of course I have. I've had him for years."

"What's he writing to you about?"

"If you'll kindly keep quiet for two seconds, if you know how," said Lancelot, "I'll tell you."

And in a clear voice which, like that of all the Mulliners, however distant from the main branch, was beautifully modulated, he read as follows:

> The Deanery,
> Bolsover, Wilts.

My dear Lancelot,

As you have, no doubt, already learned from your *Church Times*, I have been offered and have accepted the vacant Bishopric of Bongo-Bongo, in West Africa. I sail immediately to take up my new duties, which I trust will be blessed.

In these circumstances it becomes necessary for me to find a good home for my cat Webster. It is, alas, out of the question that he should accompany me, as the rigours of the climate and the lack of essential comforts might well sap a constitution which has never been robust.

I am dispatching him, therefore, to your address, my dear boy, in a straw-lined hamper, in the full confidence that you will prove a kindly and conscientious host.

With cordial good wishes,

> Your affectionate uncle,
> Theodore Bongo-Bongo

For some moments after he had finished reading this communication, a thoughtful silence prevailed in the studio.

"Of all the nerve!" she said. "I wouldn't do it."

"Why not?"

"What do you want with a cat?"

Lancelot reflected.

"It is true," he said, "that, given a free hand, I would prefer not to have my studio turned into a cattery or cat-bin. But consider the special circumstances. Relations between Uncle Theodore and self have for the last few years been a bit strained. In fact, you might say we have definitely parted brass-rags. It looks to me as if he were coming round. I should describe this letter as more or less what you might call an olive-branch. If I lush this cat up satisfactorily, shall I not be in a position later on to make a swift touch?"

"He is rich, this bean?" said Gladys, interested.

"Extremely."

"Then," said Gladys, "consider my objections withdrawn. A good stout cheque from a grateful cat-fancier would undoubtedly come in very handy. We might be able to get married this year."

"Exactly," said Lancelot. "A pretty loathsome prospect, of course; but still, as we've arranged to do it, the sooner we get it over, the better, what?"

"Absolutely."

"Then that's settled. I accept custody of cat."

"It's the only thing to do," said Gladys. "Meanwhile, can you lend me a comb? Have you such a thing in your bedroom?"

The Cat, unknown American artist (*National Gallery of Art, Washington, D.C., Collection of Edgar William and Bernice Chrysler Garbisch*)

"What do you want with a comb?"

"I got some soup in my hair at lunch. I won't be a minute."

She hurried out, and Lancelot, taking up the letter again, found that he had omitted to read a continuation of it on the back page.

It was to the following effect:

PS. In establishing Webster in your home, I am actuated by another motive than the simple desire to see to it that my faithful friend and companion is adequately provided for.

From both a moral and an educative standpoint, I am convinced that Webster's society will prove of inestimable value to you. His advent, indeed, I venture to hope, will be a turning-point in your life. Thrown, as you must be, incessantly among loose and immoral Bohemians, you will find in this cat an example of upright conduct which cannot but act as an antidote to the poison cup of temptation which is, no doubt, hourly pressed to your lips.

[29]

PPS. Cream only at midday, and fish not more than three times a week.

He was reading these words for the second time, when the front-door bell rang and he found a man on the steps with a hamper. A discreet mew from within revealed its contents, and Lancelot, carrying it into the studio, cut the strings.

"Hi!" he bellowed, going to the door.

"What's up?" shrieked his betrothed from above.

"The cat's come."

"All right. I'll be down in a jiffy."

Lancelot returned to the studio.

"What ho, Webster!" he said cheerily. "How's the boy?"

The cat did not reply. It was sitting with bent head, performing that wash and brush up which a journey by rail renders so necessary.

In order to facilitate these toilet operations, it had raised its left leg and was holding it rigidly in the air. And there flashed into Lancelot's mind an old superstition handed on to him, for what it was worth, by one of the nurses of his infancy. If, this woman had said, you creep up to a cat when its leg is in the air, and give it a pull, then you make a wish and your wish comes true in thirty days.

It was a pretty fancy, and it seemed to Lancelot that the theory might as well be put to the test. He advanced warily, therefore, and was in the act of extending his fingers for the pull, when Webster, lowering the leg, turned and raised his eyes.

He looked at Lancelot. And suddenly with sickening force there came to Lancelot the realisation of the unpardonable liberty he had been about to take.

Until this moment, though the postscript to his uncle's letter should have warned him, Lancelot Mulliner had had no suspicion of what manner of cat this was that he had taken into his home. Now, for the first time, he saw him steadily and saw him whole.

Webster was very large and very black and very composed. He conveyed the impression of being a cat of deep reserves. Descendant of a long line of ecclesiastical ancestors who had conducted their decorous courtships beneath the shadow of cathedrals and on the back walls of bishops' palaces, he had that exquisite poise which one sees in high dignitaries of the Church. His eyes were clear and steady, and seemed to pierce to the very roots of the young man's soul, filling him with a sense of guilt.

Once, long ago, in his hot childhood, Lancelot, spending his summer holidays at the Deanery, had been so far carried away by ginger-beer and original sin as to plug a senior canon in the leg with his air-gun—only to discover, on turning, that a visiting archdeacon had been a spectator of the entire incident from his immediate rear. As he felt then, when meeting the archdeacon's eye, so did he feel now as Webster's gaze played silently upon him.

Webster, it is true, had not actually raised his eyebrows. But this, Lancelot felt, was simply because he hadn't any.

He backed, blushing.

"Sorry!" he muttered.

There was a pause. Webster continued his steady scrutiny. Lancelot edged towards the door.

"Er—excuse me—just a moment . . ." he mumbled. And, sidling from the room, he ran distractedly upstairs.

"I say," said Lancelot.

"Now what?" asked Gladys.

"Have you finished with the mirror?"

"Why?"

"Well, I—er—I thought," said Lancelot, "that I might as well have a shave."

The girl looked at him, astonished.

"Shave? Why, you shaved only the day before yesterday."

"I know. But, all the same . . . I mean to say, it seems only respectful. That cat, I mean."

"What about him?"

"Well, he seems to expect it, somehow. Nothing actually said, don't you know, but you could tell by his manner. I thought a quick shave and perhaps change into my blue serge suit—"

"He's probably thirsty. Why don't you give him some milk?"

"Could one, do you think?" said Lancelot doubtful. "I mean I hardly seem to know him well enough." He paused. "I say, old girl," he went on, with a touch of hesitation.

"Hullo?"

Large Cat, who weighed $25\frac{3}{4}$ lb.

LARGE CAT.

[31]

"I know you won't mind my mentioning it, but you've got a few spots of ink on your nose."

"Of course I have. I always have spots of ink on my nose."

"Well . . . you don't think . . . a quick scrub with a bit of pumice-stone . . . I mean to say, you know how important first impressions are . . ."

The girl stared.

"Lancelot Mulliner," she said, "if you think I'm going to skin my nose to the bone just to please a mangy cat—"

"Sh!" cried Lancelot, in agony.

"Here, let me go down and look at him," said Gladys petulantly.

As they re-entered the studio, Webster was gazing with an air of quiet distaste at an illustration from *La Vie Parisienne* which adorned one of the walls. Lancelot tore it down hastily.

Gladys looked at Webster in an unfriendly way.

"So that's the blighter!"

"Sh!"

"If you want to know what I think," said Gladys, "that cat's been living too high. Doing himself a dashed sight too well. You'd better cut his rations down a bit."

In substance, her criticism was not unjustified, Certainly, there was about Webster more than a suspicion of embonpoint. He had that air of portly well-being which we associate with those who dwell in cathedral closes. But Lancelot winced uncomfortably. He had so hoped that Gladys would make a good impression, and here she was, starting right off by saying the tactless thing.

He longed to explain to Webster that it was only her way; that in the Bohemian circles of which she was such an ornament genial chaff of a personal order was accepted and, indeed, relished. But it was too late. The mischief had been done. Webster turned in a pointed manner and withdrew silently behind the chesterfield.

Gladys, all unconscious, was making preparations for departure.

"Well, bung-ho," she said lightly. "See you in three weeks. I suppose you and that cat'll both be out on the tiles the moment my back's turned."

"Please! Please!" moaned Lancelot. "Please!"

He had caught sight of the tip of a black tail protruding from behind the chesterfield. It was twitching slightly, and Lancelot could read it like a book. With a sickening sense of dismay, he knew that Webster had formed a snap judgment of his fiancée and condemned her as frivolous and unworthy.

It was some ten days later than Bernard Worple, the neo-Vorticist sculptor, lunching at the Puce Ptarmigan, ran into Rodney Scollop, the powerful young surrealist. And after talking for a while of their art:

"What's all this I hear about Lancelot Mulliner?" asked Worple. "There's a wild story going about that he was seen shaved in the middle of the week. Nothing in it, I suppose?"

Scollop looked grave. He had been on the point of mentioning Lancelot himself, for he loved the lad and was deeply exercised about him.

"It is perfectly true," he said.

"It sounds incredible."

Scollop leaned forward. His fine face was troubled.

"Shall I tell you something, Worple?"

"What?"

"I know for an absolute fact," said Scollop, "that Lancelot Mulliner now shaves every morning."

Worple pushed aside the spaghetti which he was wreathing about him and through the gap stared at his companion.

"Every morning?"

"Every single morning. I looked in on him myself the other day, and there he was, neatly dressed in blue serge and shaved to the core. And, what is more, I got the distinct impression that he had used talcum powder afterwards."

"You don't mean that!"

"I do. And shall I tell you something else? There was a book lying open on the table. He tried to hide it, but he wasn't quick enough. It was one of those etiquette books!"

"An etiquette book!"

"*Polite Behaviour*, by Constance, Lady Bodbank."

Worple unwound a stray tendril of spaghetti from about his left ear. He was deeply agitated. Like Scollop, he loved Lancelot.

"He'll be dressing for dinner next!" he exclaimed.

"I have every reason to believe," said Scollop gravely, "that he does dress for dinner. At any rate, a man closely resembling him was seen furtively buying three stiff collars and a black tie at Hope Brothers in the King's Road last Tuesday."

Worple pushed his chair back, and rose. His manner was determined.

"Scollop," he said, "we are friends of Mulliner's, you and I. It is evident from what you tell me that subversive influences are at work and that never has he needed our friendship more. Shall we not go round and see him immediately?"

"It was what I was about to suggest myself," said Rodney Scollop.

Twenty minutes later they were in Lancelot's studio, and with a significant glance Scollop drew his companion's notice to their host's appearance. Lancelot Mulliner was neatly, even foppishly, dressed in blue serge with creases down the trouser-legs, and his chin, Worple saw with a pang, gleamed smoothly in the afternoon light.

At the sight of his friends' cigars, Lancelot exhibited unmistakable concern.

"You don't mind throwing those away, I'm sure," he said pleadingly.

Rodney Scollop drew himself up a little haughtily.

"And since when", he asked, "have the best fourpenny cigars in Chelsea not been good enough for you?"

Lancelot hastened to soothe him.

"It isn't me," he exclaimed. "It's Webster. My cat. I happen to know he objects to tobacco smoke. I had to give up my pipe in deference to his views."

Bernard Worple snorted.

"Are you trying to tell us," he sneered, "that Lancelot Mulliner allows himself to be dictated to by a blasted cat?"

"Hush!" cried Lancelot, trembling. "If you knew how he disapproves of strong language!"

"Where is this cat?" asked Rodney Scollop. "Is that the animal?" he said, pointing out of the window to where, in the yard, a tough-looking Tom with tattered ears stood mewing in a hardboiled way out of the corner of its mouth.

"Good heavens, no!" said Lancelot. "That is an alley cat which comes round here from time to time to lunch at the dustbin. Webster is quite different. Webster has a natural dignity and repose of manner. Webster is a cat who prides himself on always being well turned out and whose high principles and lofty ideals shine from his eyes like beacon fires . . ." And then suddenly, with an abrupt change of manner, Lancelot broke down and in a low voice added, "Curse him! Curse him! Curse him! Curse him!"

[33]

The Painter with a Lovable Cat, I. Kay

Worple looked at Scollop. Scollop looked at Worple.

"Come, old man," said Scollop, laying a gentle hand on Lancelot's bowed shoulder. "We are your friends. Confide in us."

"Tell us all," said Worple. "What's the matter?"

Lancelot uttered a bitter, mirthless laugh.

"You want to know what's the matter? Listen, then. I'm cat-pecked!"

"Cat-pecked?"

"You've heard of men being hen-pecked, haven't you?" said Lancelot with a touch of irritation. "Well, I'm cat-pecked."

And in broken accents he told his story. He sketched the history of his association with Webster from the latter's first entry into the studio. Confident now that the animal was not within earshot, he unbosomed himself without reserve.

"It's something in the beast's eye," he said in a shaking voice. "Something hypnotic. He casts a spell upon me. He gazes at me and disapproves. Little by little, bit by bit, I am degenerating under his influence from a wholesome, self-respecting artist into . . . well, I don't know what you call it. Suffice it to say that I have given up smoking, that I have ceased to wear carpet slippers and go about without a collar, that I never dream of sitting down to my frugal evening

[34]

meal without dressing, and"—he choked— "I have sold my ukulele."

"Not that!" said Worple, paling.

"Yes," said Lancelot. "I felt he considered it frivolous."

There was a long silence.

"Mulliner," said Scollop, "this is more serious that I had supposed. We must brood upon your case."

"It may be possible", said Worple, "to find a way out."

Lancelot shook his head hopelessly.

"There is no way out. I have explored every avenue. The only thing that could possibly free me from this intolerable bondage would be if once—just once—I could catch that cat unbending. If once—merely once—it would lapse in my presence from its austere dignity for but a single instant, I feel that the spell would be broken. But what hope is there of that?" cried Lancelot passionately. "You were pointing just now to that alley cat in the yard. There stands one who has strained every nerve and spared no effort to break down Webster's inhuman self-control. I have heard that animal say things to him which you would think no cat with red blood in its veins would suffer for an instant. And Webster merely looks at him like a Suffragan Bishop eyeing an erring choirboy and turns his head and falls into a refreshing sleep."

He broke off with a dry sob. Worple, always an optimist, attempted in his kindly way to minimise the tragedy.

"Ah, well," he said. "It's bad, of course, but still, I suppose there is no actual harm in shaving and dressing for dinner and so on. Many great artists . . . Whistler, for example—"

"Wait!" cried Lancelot. "You have not heard the worst."

He rose feverishly, and, going to the easel, disclosed the portrait of Brenda Carberry-Pirbright.

"Take a look at that," he said, "and tell me what you think of her."

His two friends surveyed the face before them in silence. Miss Carberry-Pirbright was a young woman of prim and glacial aspect. One sought in vain for her reasons for wanting to have her portrait painted. It would be a most unpleasant thing to have about any house.

Scollop broke the silence.

"Friend of yours?"

"I can't stand the sight of her," said Lancelot vehemently.

"Then," said Scollop, "I may speak frankly. I think she's a pill."

"A blister," said Worple.

"A boil and a disease," said Scollop, summing up.

Lancelot laughed hackingly.

"You have described her to a nicety. She stands for everything most alien to my artist soul. She gives me a pain in the neck. I'm going to marry her."

"What!" cried Scollop.

"But you're going to marry Gladys Bingley," said Worple.

"Webster thinks not," said Lancelot bitterly. "At their first meeting he weighed Gladys in the balance and found her wanting. And the moment he saw Brenda Carberry-Pirbright he stuck his tail up at right angles, uttered a cordial gargle, and rubbed his head against her leg. Then turning, he looked at me. I could read that glance. I knew what was in his mind. From that moment he has been doing everything in his power to arrange the match."

"But, Mulliner," said Worple, always eager to point out the bright side, "why should this girl want to marry a wretched, scrubby, hard-up footler like you? Have courage, Mulliner. It is simply a question of time before you repel and sicken her."

[35]

Lancelot shook his head.

"No," he said. "You speak like a true friend, Worple, but you do not understand. Old Ma Carberry-Pirbright, this exhibit's mother, who chaperons her at the sittings, discovered at an early date my relationship to my Uncle Theodore, who, as you know, has got it in gobs. She knows well enough that some day I shall be a rich man. She used to know my Uncle Theodore when he was Vicar of St Botolph's in Knightsbridge, and from the very first she assumed towards me the repellent chumminess of an old family friend. She was always trying to lure me to her At Homes, her Sunday luncheons, her little dinners. Once she actually suggested that I should escort her and her beastly daughter to the Royal Academy."

He laughed bitterly. The mordant witticisms of Lancelot Mulliner at the expense of the Royal Academy were quoted from Tite Street in the south to Holland Park in the north and eastward as far as Bloomsbury.

"To all these overtures," resumed Lancelot, "I remained firmly unresponsive. My attitude was from the start one of frigid aloofness. I did not actually say in so many words that I would rather be dead in a ditch than at one of her At Homes, but my manner indicated it. And I was just beginning to think I had choked her off when in crashed Webster and upset everything. Do you know how many times I have been to that infernal house in the last week? Five. Webster seemed to wish it. I tell you, I am a lost man."

He buried his face in his hands. Scollop touched Worple on the arm, and together the two men stole silently out.

"Bad!" said Worple.

"Very bad," said Scollop.

"It seems incredible."

"Oh, no. Cases of this kind are, alas, by no means uncommon among those who, like Mulliner, possess to a marked degree the highly-strung, ultra-sensitive artistic temperament. A friend of mine, a rhythmical interior decorator, once rashly consented to put his aunt's parrot up at his studio while she was away visiting friends in the north of England. She was a woman of strong evangelical views, which the bird had imbibed from her. It had a way of putting its head on one side, making a noise like someone drawing a cork from a bottle, and asking my friend if he was saved. To cut a long story short, I happened to call on him a month later and he had installed a harmonium in his studio and was singing hymns, ancient and modern, in a rich tenor, while the parrot, standing on one leg on its perch, took the bass. A very sad affair. We were all much upset about it."

Worple shuddered.

"You appal me, Scollop! Is there nothing we can do?"

Rodney Scollop considered for a moment.

"We might wire Gladys Bingley to come home at once. She might possibly reason with the unhappy man. A woman's gentle influence . . . Yes, we could do that. Look in at the post office on your way home and send Gladys a telegram. I'll owe you for my half of it."

In the studio they had left, Lancelot Mulliner was staring dumbly at a black shape which had just entered the room. He had the appearance of a man with his back to the wall.

"No!" he was crying. "No! I'm dashed if I do!"

Webster continued to look at him.

"Why should I?" demanded Lancelot weakly.

Webster's gaze did not flicker.

"Oh, all right," said Lancelot sullenly.

He passed from the room with leaden feet, and, proceeding upstairs, changed into morning clothes and a top hat. Then, with a gardenia in his buttonhole, he made his way to 11 Maxton Square, where Mrs Carberry-Pirbright was giving one of her intimate little teas ("just a few friends") to meet Clara Throckmorton Stooge, authoress of *A Strong Man's Kiss*.

Gladys Bingley was lunching at her hotel in Antibes when Worple's telegram arrived. It occasioned her the gravest concern.

Exactly what it was all about she was unable to gather, for emotion had made Bernard Worple rather incoherent. There were moments, reading it, when she fancied that Lancelot had met with a serious accident; others when the solution seemed to be that he had sprained his brain to such an extent that rival lunatic asylums were competing eagerly for his custom; others, again, when Worple appeared to be suggesting that he had gone into partnership with his cat to start a harem. But one fact emerged clearly. Her loved one was in serious trouble of some kind, and his best friends were agreed that only her immediate return could save him.

Gladys did not hesitate. Within half an hour of the receipt of the telegram she had packed her trunk, removed a piece of asparagus from her right eyebrow, and was negotiating for accommodation on the first train going north.

Arriving in London, her first impulse was to go straight to Lancelot. But a natural feminine curiosity urged her, before doing so, to call upon Bernard Worple and have light thrown on some of the more abstruse passages in the telegram.

Worple, in his capacity of author, may have tended towards obscurity, but, when confining himself to the spoken word, he told a plain story well and clearly. Five minutes of his society enabled Gladys to obtain a firm grasp on the salient facts, and there appeared on her face that grim, tight-lipped expression which is seen only on the faces of fiancées who have come back from a short holiday to discover that their dear one has been straying in their absence from the straight and narrow path.

"Brenda Carberry-Pirbright, eh?" said Gladys, with ominous calm. "I'll give him Brenda Carberry-Pirbright! My gosh, if one can't go off to Antibes for the merest breather without having one's betrothed getting it up his nose and starting to act like a Mormon Elder, it begins to look a pretty tough world for a girl."

Kind-hearted Bernard Worple did his best.

"I blame the cat," he said. "Lancelot, to my mind, is more sinned against than sinning. I consider him to be acting under undue influence or duress."

"How like a man!" said Gladys. "Shoving it all off on to an innocent cat!"

"Lancelot says it has a sort of something in its eye."

"Well, when I meet Lancelot," said Gladys, "he'll find that I have a sort of something in my eye."

She went out, breathing flame quiety through her nostrils. Worple, saddened, heaved a sigh and resumed his neo-Vorticist sculpting.

It was some five minutes later that Gladys, passing through Maxton Square on her way to Bott Street, stopped suddenly in her tracks. The sight she had seen was enough to make any fiancée do so.

Along the pavement leading to No. 11 two figures were advancing. Or three, if you counted a morose-looking dog of a semi-dachshund nature which preceded them, attached to a leash. One of the figures was that of Lancelot Mulliner, natty in grey herring-bone tweed and a new Homburg hat. It was he who held the leash. The other Gladys recognised from the portrait which she had seen on Lancelot's easel as that modern Du Barry, that notorious wrecker of homes and breaker-up of love-nests, Brenda Carberry-Pirbright.

[37]

The next moment they had mounted the steps of No. 11, and had gone in to tea, possibly with a little music.

It was perhaps an hour and a half later that Lancelot, having wrenched himself with difficulty from the lair of the Philistines, sped homeward in a swift taxi. As always after an extended tête-à-tête with Miss Carberry-Pirbright, he felt dazed and bewildered, as if he had been swimming in a sea of glue and had swallowed a good deal of it. All he could think of clearly was that he wanted a drink and that the materials for that drink were in the cupboard behind the chesterfield in his studio.

He paid the cab and charged in with his tongue rattling dryly against his front teeth. And there before him was Gladys Bingley, whom he had supposed far, far away.

"You!" exclaimed Lancelot.

"Yes, me!" said Gladys.

Her long vigil had not helped to restore the girl's equanimity. Since arriving at the studio she had had leisure to tap her foot three thousand, one hundred and forty-two times on the carpet, and the number of bitter smiles which had flitted across her face was nine hundred and eleven. She was about ready for the battle of the century.

She rose and faced him all the woman in her flashing from her eyes.

"Well, you Casanova!" she said.

"You who?" said Lancelot.

"Don't say 'Yoo-hoo!' to me!" cried Gladys. "Keep that for your Brenda Carberry-Pirbright. Yes, I know all about it, Lancelot Don Juan Henry the Eighth Mulliner! I saw you with her just now. I hear that you and she are inseparable. Bernard Worple says you said you were going to marry her."

"You mustn't believe everything a neo-Vorticist sculptor tells you," quavered Lancelot.

"I'll bet you're going back to dinner there tonight," said Gladys.

She had spoken at a venture, basing the charge purely on a possessive cock of the head which she had noticed in Brenda Carberry-Pirbright at their recent encounter. There, she had said to herself at the time, had gone a girl who was about to invite—or had just invited—Lancelot Mulliner to dine quietly and take her to the pictures afterwards. But the shot went home. Lancelot hung his head.

"There was some talk of it," he admitted.

"Ah!" exclaimed Gladys.

Lancelot's eyes were haggard.

"I don't want to go," he pleaded. "Honestly, I don't. But Webster insists."

"Webster!"

"Yes, Webster. If I attempt to evade the appointment, he will sit in front of me and look at me."

"Tchah!"

"Well, he will. Ask him for yourself."

Gladys tapped her foot six times in rapid succession on the carpet, bringing the total to three thousand, one hundred and forty-eight. Her manner had changed and was now dangerously calm.

"Lancelot Mulliner," she said, "you have your choice. Me, on the one hand, Brenda Carberry-Pirbright on the other. I offer you a home where you will be able to smoke in bed, spill the ashes on the floor, wear pyjamas and carpet slippers all day and shave only on Sunday mornings. From her, what have you to hope? A house in South Kensington—possibly the

[38]

Advancing Cat, Louis Wain (© *Guttman Maclay Collection, Institute of Psychiatry, London*)

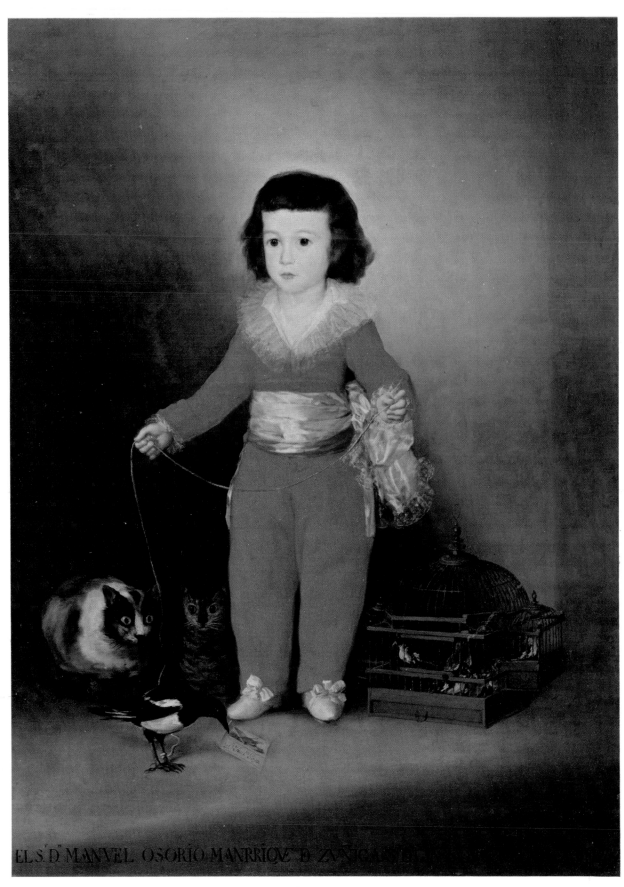

Don Manuel Osorio de Zuñiga, Francisco de Goya (*The Metropolitan Museum of Art, The Jules S. Bache Collection, 1949*)

Cat as Painter, 1890

Brompton Road—probably with her mother living with you. A life that will be one long round of stiff collars and tight shoes, of morning coats and top hats."

Lancelot quivered, but she went on remorselessly.

"You will be at home on alternate Thursdays, and will be expected to hand the cucumber sandwiches. Every day you will air the dog, till you become a confirmed dog-airer. You will dine out in Bayswater and go for the summer to Bournemouth or Dinard. Choose well, Lancelot Mulliner! I will leave you to think it over. But one last word. If by seven-thirty on the dot you have not presented yourself at 6a Garbidge Mews ready to take me out to dinner at the Ham and Beef, I shall know what to think and shall act accordingly."

And brushing the cigarette ashes from her chin, the girl strode haughtily from the room.

"Gladys!" cried Lancelot.

But she had gone.

For some minutes Lancelot Mulliner remained where he was, stunned. Then, insistently, there came to him the recollection that he had not had that drink. He rushed to the cupboard and produced the bottle. He uncorked it, and was pouring out a lavish stream, when a movement on the floor below him attracted his attention.

Webster was standing there, looking up at him. And in his eyes was that familiar expression of quiet rebuke.

"Scarcely what I have been accustomed to at the Deanery," he seemed to be saying.

Lancelot stood paralysed. The feeling of being bound hand and foot, of being caught in a snare from which there was no escape, had become more poignant than ever. The bottle fell from his nerveless fingers and rolled across the floor, spilling its contents in an amber river, but he was too heavy in spirit to notice it. With a gesture such as Job might have made on discovering a new boil, he crossed to the window and stood looking moodily out.

Then, turning with a sigh, he looked at Webster again—and, looking, stood spell-bound.

The spectacle which he beheld was of a kind to stun a stronger man than Lancelot Mulliner. At first, he shrank from believing his eyes. Then, slowly, came the realisation that what he saw was no mere figment of a disordered imagination. This unbelievable thing was actually happening.

Webster sat crouched upon the floor beside the widening pool of whisky. But it was not horror and disgust that had caused him to crouch. He was crouched because, crouching, he could get nearer to the stuff and obtain crisper action. His tongue was moving in and out like a piston.

And then abruptly, for one fleeting instant, he stopped lapping and glanced up at Lancelot, and across his face there flitted a quick smile—so genial, so intimate, so full of jovial camaraderie, that the young man found himself automatically smiling back, and not only smiling but winking. And in answer to that wink Webster winked too—a whole-hearted, roguish wink that said as plainly as if he had spoken the words:

"How long has this been going on?"

Then with a slight hiccough he turned back to the task of getting his drink before it soaked into the floor.

Into the murky soul of Lancelot Mulliner there poured a sudden flood of sunshine. It was as if a great burden had been lifted from his shoulders. The intolerable obsession of the last two weeks had ceased to oppress him, and he felt a free man. At the eleventh hour the reprieve had come. Webster, that seeming pillar of austere virtue, was one of the boys, after all. Never again would Lancelot quail beneath his eye. He had the goods on him.

Webster, like the stag at eve, had now drunk his fill. He had left the pool of alchohol and

The Artist's Studio (detail), Gustave Courbet (*Musée du Louvre, Paris*)

was walking round in slow, meditative circles. From time to time he mewed tentatively, as if he were trying to say "British Constitution". His failure to articulate the syllables appeared to tickle him, for at the end of each attempt he would utter a slow, amused chuckle. It was about this moment that he suddenly broke into a rhythmic dance, not unlike the old Saraband.

It was an interesting spectacle, and at any other time Lancelot would have watched it raptly. But now he was busy at his desk, writing a brief note to Mrs Carberry-Pirbright, the burden of which was that if she thought he was coming within a mile of her foul house that night or any other night she had vastly underrated the dodging powers of Lancelot Mulliner.

And what of Webster? The Demon Rum now had him in an iron grip. A lifetime of abstinence had rendered him a ready victim to the fatal fluid. He had now reached the stage when geniality gives way to belligerence. The rather foolish smile had gone from his face, and in its stead there lowered a fighting frown. For a few moments he stood on his hind legs, looking about him for a suitable adversary: then, losing all vestiges of self-control, he ran five times round the the room at a high rate of speed and, falling foul of a small footstool, attacked it with the utmost ferocity, sparing neither tooth nor claw.

But Lancelot did not see him. Lancelot was not there. Lancelot was out in Bott Street, hailing a cab.

"6a Garbidge Mews, Fulham," said Lancelot to the driver.

On Lutestrings Catt-Eaten

Thomas Master

Are these the strings that poets feigne
Have clear'd the Ayre, and calm'd the mayne?
Charm'd wolves, and from the mountaine creasts
Made forests dance with all their beasts?
Could these neglected shreads you see
Inspire a Lute of Ivorie
And make it speake? Oh! think then what
Hath beene committed by my catt,
Who, in the silence of this night
Hath gnawne these cords, and marr'd them quite;
Leaving such reliques as may be
For fretts, not for my lute, but me.
Pusse, I will curse thee; may'st thou dwell
With some dry Hermit in a cell

Where Ratt neere peep'd, where mouse neere fedd,
And flyes goes supperlesse to bedd;
Or with some close-par'd Brother, where
Thou'lt fast each Saboath in the yeare;
Or else, prophane, be hang'd on Munday,
For butchering a mouse on Sunday;
Or May'st thou tumble from some tower,
And misse to light upon all fower,
Taking a fall that may untie
Eight of nine lives, and let them flye;
Or may the midnight embers sindge
Thy daintie coate, or Jane beswinge
Thy hide, when she shall take thee biting
Her cheese clouts, or her house beshiting.
What, was there neere a ratt nor mouse,
Nor Buttery ope? nought in the house
But harmelesse Lutestrings could suffice
Thy paunch, and draw thy glaring eyes?
Did not thy conscious stomach finde
Nature prophan'd, that kind with kind
Should stanch his hunger? thinke on that,
Thou caniball, and Cyclops catt.
For know, thou wretch, that every string
Is a catt-gutt, which art doth spinne
Into a thread; and how suppose
Dunstan, that snuff'd the divell's nose,
Should bid these strings revive, as once
He did the calfe, from naked bones;
Or I, to plague thee for thy sinne,
Should draw a circle, and beginne
To conjure, for I am, look to't,
An Oxford scholler, and can doo't.
Then with three setts of mapps and mowes,
Seaven of odd words, and motley showes,
A thousand tricks, that may be taken
From Faustus, Lambe, or Fryar Bacon:
I should beginne to call my strings
My catlings, and my mynikins;
And they recalled, straight should fall
To mew, to purr, to catterwaule
From puss's belly. Sure as death,
Pusse should be an Engastranith;
Pusse should be sent for to the king
For a strange bird, or some rare thing.
Pusse should be sought to farre and neere,
As she some cunning woman were.
Pusse should be carried up and downe,

The Cats' Concert (British Library, London)

From shire to shire, from Towne to Towne,
Like to the camell, Leane as Hagg,
The Elephant, or Apish negg,
For a strange sight; pusse should be sung
In Lousy Ballads, midst the Throng
At markets, with as good a grace
As Agincourt, or Chevy-chase.
The Troy-sprung Brittan would forgoe
His pedigree he chaunteth soe,
And singe that Merlin—long deceast—
Returned is in a nyne-liv'd beast.

    Thus, pusse, thou seest what might betyde thee;
But I forbeare to hurt or chide thee;
For may be pusse was melancholy
And so to make her blythe and jolly,
Finding these strings, shee'ld have a fitt
Of mirth; nay, pusse, if that were it,
Thus I revenge mee, that as thou
Hast played on them, I've plaid on you;
And as thy touch was nothing fine,
Soe I've but scratch'd these notes of mine.

[44]

A Cat Piano, 1883

The Diminutive Lyon or Catus, *the Cat*

William Salmon

I. It is called in Hebrew, בטול מחנר, *Catul, Schanar*; in Chaldean, חתול, *pl.* חתוליז, *Chatul, pl. Chatulin*; in Greek, Κάτλης, αἴλουρος; in Latin, *Catus, felis*; in English; *the Cat*, but the wild Cat is supposed to be called in Hebrew, אייס, *Jim. Isa.* 13, 22, and 34, 14. for so *Arius Montanus* translates it; as for *Kat* or *Cat*, it is the most usual name that almost all Nations call it by.

II. It is bred and is an Inhabitant of almost all Countries in the World, all *Cats* were at first wild, but were at length tamed by the industry of Mankind; it is a Beast of prey, even the tame one, more especially the wild, it being in the opinion of many nothing but a diminutive Lyon.

[45]

Cat from *The Historie of Foure-Footed Beastes*, 1607, by Edward Topsell

[46]

III. It is now said to be of three kinds, 1. *The tame Cat*. 2. *The wild wood Cat*. 3. *The Cat of Mountain*, all which are of one nature, and agree much in one Shape, save as to their magnitude, the *wild Cat* being larger much than the Tame, and the *Cat of Mountain* much larger than the *wild Cat*.

IV. It has a broad Face almost like a Lyon, short Ears, large Whiskers, shining Eyes, short smooth Hair, long Tail, rough Tongue, and armed on its Feet with Claws, being a crafty, subtle watchful Creature, very loving and familiar with Man-kind, the mortal enemy to the Rat, Mouse, and all sorts of Birds, which it seizes on as its prey. As to its Eyes, Authors say that they shine in the Night, and see better at the full, and more dimly at the change of the Moon; as also that the Cat doth vary his Eyes with the Sun, the Apple of its Eye being long at Sun rise, round towards Noon, and not to be seen at all at night, but the whole Eye shining in the night. These appearances of the Cats Eyes I am sure are true, but whether they answer to the times of the day, I never observed.

V. It is a neat and cleanly creature, often licking it self, to keep it fair and clean, and washing its Face with its fore-feet; the best are such as are of a fair and large kind, and of an exquisite Tabby color, called *Cyprus* Cats. They usually generate in the winter Season, making a great noise, go 56 Days or 8 weeks with young, and bring forth 2, 3, 4, 5, 6, or more at a time, they cover their excrements, and love to keep their old habitations.

VI. *Its Flesh* is not usually eaten, yet in some Countries it is accounted an excellent Dish, but the Brain is said to be poisonous, causing madness, stupidity, and loss of memory, which is cured only by vomiting, and taking musk in Wine. The Flesh applied easeth the pain of Hæmorrhoids and the back, and salted, beaten, and applied, draws Thorns, &c. out of the Flesh, and is said particularly to help the Gout, especially that of the wild Cat.

VII. *The Fat* is hot, dry, emollient, discussive, and Anodyne: ℞ *Cat's Grease*, ℥ij. *Palm Oyl*, ℥β. *Oil of Anniseed*, ʒj. *mix them*; it dissolves tumors, eases pain, and prevails against nodes in the Shin, and the cold Gout.

VIII. *The Head*: ℞ *the Ashes of a Cat's Head* ℥j. *white vitriol in fine Pouder*, Saccharum Saturni *ana* ℈j. *mix them for a Pouder*; or mix them with Honey for a Balsam, blown into the Eyes, or annointed thrice aday; it cures Blindness, and most Diseases of the Eyes, as the Pin and Web, Pearls, Clouds, Films, &c.

IX. *The Liver*: ℞ *the Ashes, or rather pouder of it*, ℥j. *Borax, Nitre, Volatile Sal Armoniack, Pouder of Elecampane, Roots of Bay-berries*, ana ʒij. *mix them*. Dose ʒij. in any convenient Vehicle, against Gravel and stoppage of Urine.

X. *The Gall*: ℞ of *Cat's Gall*, ℥β. of our Aqua Regulata ℥ij. *Honey*, ʒj. *mix them for a* Collyrium to wash the Eyes often with against Pearls, Films, Blindness, and Dimness of the sight: ℞ *Cat's Gall* ℥β. Colo quintida, *Fine Aloes, Ana* q.s. *Musk gr.* xvi. *mix and make a pessary*. It brings away the birth and after birth, and extracts a Mola.

XI. *The Blood*, some affirms it kills Worms in the Nose, and other places of the Skin: ℞ *the Bloud*

[47]

of the Tail of a Bore-Cat gut. x. *Salt of Man's Skull, gr.* vj. *pouder of Ox horns,* gr. 10. *mix them for a Dose.* It is said to cure the Falling-Sickness.

XII. *The Dung and Urine:* ℞ *Pouder of Cats Dung,* ℥j. *Mustard-seed in Pouder,* ℥iij. *Juice of Onions,* ℥ii. *Bears Grease enough to make an Oyntment.* It cures Baldness and the Alopecia.

III

 Cat's Games

Poem

William Carlos Williams

As the cat
climbed over
the top of

the jamcloset
first the right
forefoot

carefully
then the hind
stepped down

into the pit of
the empty
flowerpot

The White Cat

W. W. Jacobs

The traveller stood looking from the taproom window of the *Cauliflower* at the falling rain. The village street below was empty, and everything was quiet with the exception of the garrulous old man smoking with much enjoyment on the settle behind him.

"It'll do a power o' good," said the ancient, craning his neck round the edge of the settle and turning a bleared eye on the window. "I ain't like some folk; I never did mind a drop o' rain."

The traveller grunted and, returning to the settle opposite the old man, fell to lazily stroking a cat which had strolled in attracted by the warmth of the small fire which smouldered in the grate.

"He's a good mouser," said the old man, "but I expect that Smith the landlord would sell 'im to anybody for arf a crown, but we 'ad a cat in Claybury once that you couldn't ha' bought for a hundred golden sovereigns."

The traveller continued to caress the cat.

"A white cat, with one yaller eye and one blue one," continued the old man. "It sounds queer, but it's as true as I sit 'ere wishing that I 'ad another mug o' ale as good as the last you gave me."

The traveller, with a start that upset the cat's nerves, finished his own mug, and then ordered both to be refilled. He stirred the fire into a blaze, and, lighting his pipe and putting one foot on to the hob, prepared to listen.

It used to belong to old man Clark, young Joe Clark's uncle, said the ancient, smacking his lips delicately over the ale and extending a tremulous claw to the tobacco-pouch pushed towards him; and he was never tired of showing it off to people. He used to call it 'is blue-eyed darling, and the fuss 'e made o' that cat was sinful.

Young Joe Clark couldn't bear it, but being down in 'is uncle's will for five cottages and a bit o' land bringing in about forty pounds a year, he 'ad to 'ide his feelings and pretend as he

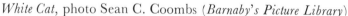

White Cat, photo Sean C. Coombs (*Barnaby's Picture Library*)

loved it. He used to take it little drops o' cream and tid-bits o' meat, and old Clark was so pleased that 'e promised 'im that he should 'ave the cat along with all the other property when 'e was dead.

Young Joe said he couldn't thank 'im enough, and the old man, who 'ad been ailing a long time, made 'im come up every day to teach 'im 'ow to take care of it arter he was gone. He taught Joe 'ow to cook its meat and then chop it up fine; 'ow it liked a clean saucer every time for its milk; and 'ow he wasn't to make a noise when it was asleep.

"Take care your children don't worry it, Joe," he ses one day, very sharp. "One o' your boys was pulling its tail this morning, and I want you to clump his 'ead for 'im."

"Which one was it?" ses Joe.

"The slobbery-nosed one," ses old Clark.

"I'll give 'im a clout as soon as I get 'ome," ses Joe, who was very fond of 'is children.

"Go and fetch 'im and do it 'ere," ses the old man; "that'll teach 'im to love animals."

Joe went off 'ome to fetch the boy, and arter his mother 'ad washed his face, and wiped his nose, an' put a clean pinneyfore on 'im, he took 'im to 'is uncle's and clouted his 'ead for 'im. Arter that Joe and 'is wife 'ad words all night long, and next morning old Clark, coming in from the garden, was just in time to see 'im kick the cat right across the kitchen.

He could 'ardly speak for a minute, and when 'e could Joe see plain wot a fool he'd been. Fust of all 'e called Joe every name he could think of—which took 'im a long time—and then he ordered 'im out of 'is house.

"You shall 'ave my money wen your betters have done with it," he ses, "and not afore. That's all you've done for yourself."

Joe Clark didn't know wot he meant at the time, but when old Clark died three months afterwards 'e found out. His uncle 'ad made a new will and left everything to old George Barstow for as long as the cat lived, providing that he took care of it. When the cat was dead the property was to go to Joe.

The cat was only two years old at the time, and George Barstow, who was arf crazy with joy, said it shouldn't be 'is fault if it didn't live another twenty years.

The funny thing was the quiet way Joe Clark took it. He didn't seem to be at all cut up about it, and when Henery Walker said it was a shame, 'e said he didn't mind, and that George Barstow was a old man, and he was quite welcome to 'ave the property as long as the cat lived.

"It must come to me by the time I'm an old man," he ses, "and that's all I care about."

Henery Walker went off, and as 'e passed the cottage where old Clark used to live, and which George Barstow 'ad moved into, 'e spoke to the old man over the palings and told 'im wot Joe Clark 'ad said. George Barstow only grunted and went on stooping and prying over 'is front garden.

"Bin and lost something?" ses Henery Walker, watching 'im.

"No; I'm finding," ses George Barstow, very fierce, and picking up something. "That's the fifth bit o' powdered liver I've found in my garden this morning."

Henery Walker went off whistling, and the opinion he'd 'ad o' Joe Clark began to improve. He spoke to Joe about it that arternoon, and Joe said that if 'e ever accused 'im o' such a thing again he'd knock 'is 'ead off. He said that he 'oped the cat 'ud live to be a hundred, and that 'e'd no more think of giving it poisoned meat than Henery Walker would of paying for 'is drink so long as 'e could get anybody else to do it for 'im.

They 'ad bets up at this 'ere *Cauliflower* public-'ouse that evening as to 'ow long that cat 'ud live. Nobody gave it more than a month, and Bill Chambers sat and thought o' so many ways o' killing it on the sly that it was wunnerful to hear 'im.

George Barstow took fright when he 'eard of them, and the care 'e took o' that cat was wunnerful to behold. Arf its time it was shut up in the back bedroom, and the other arf George Barstow was fussing arter it till that cat got to hate 'im like pison. Instead o' giving up work as he'd thought to do, 'e told Henery Walker that 'e'd never worked so 'ard in his life.

"Wot about fresh air and exercise for it?" ses Henery.

"Wot about Joe Clark?" ses George Barstow. "I'm tied 'and and foot. I dursent leave the house for a moment. I ain't been to the *Cauliflower* since I've 'ad it, and three times I got out o' bed last night to see if it was safe."

"Mark my words," ses Henery Walker, "if that cat don't 'ave exercise, you'll lose it."

"I shall lose it if it does 'ave exercise," ses George Barstow, "that I know."

A Blockade Runner, Briton Rivière (*Tate Gallery, London*)

He sat down thinking arter Henery Walker 'ad gone, and then he 'ad a little collar and chain made for it, and took it out for a walk. Pretty nearly every dog in Claybury went with 'em, and the cat was in such a state o' mind afore they got 'ome he couldn't do anything with it. It 'ad a fit as soon as they got indoors, and George Barstow, who 'ad read about children's fits in the almanac, gave it a warm bath. It brought it round immediate, and then it began to tear round the room and up and down stairs till George Barstow was afraid to go near it.

[54]

Charles Waterton, Naturalist, C. W. Peale (*National Portrait Gallery, London*)

Kitty Fisher, Nathaniel Hone (*National Portrait Gallery, London*)

It was so bad that evening, sneezing, that George Barstow sent for Bill Chambers, who'd got a good name for doctoring animals, and asked 'im to give it something. Bill said he'd got some powders at 'ome that would cure it at once, and he went and fetched 'em and mixed one up with a bit o' butter.

"That's the way to give a cat medicine," he ses; "smear it with butter and then it'll lick it off, powder and all."

He was just going to rub it on the cat when George Barstow caught 'old of 'is arm and stopped 'im.

"How do I know it ain't pison?" he ses. "You're a friend o' Joe Clark's, and for all I know he may ha' paid you to pison it."

"I wouldn't do such a thing," ses Bill. "You ought to know me better than that."

"All right," ses George Barstow; "you eat it then, and I'll give you two shillings instead o' one. You can easy mix some more."

"Not me," ses Bill Chambers, making a face.

"Well, three shillings, then," ses George Barstow, getting more and more suspicious like; "four shillings—five shillings."

Bill Chambers shook his 'ead, and George Barstow, more and more certain he 'ad caught 'im trying to kill 'is cat and that 'e wouldn't eat the stuff, rose 'im up to ten shillings.

Bill looked at the butter and then 'e looked at the ten shillings on the table, and at last he shut 'is eyes and gulped it down and put the money in 'is pocket.

"You see, I 'ave to be careful, Bill," ses George Barstow, rather upset.

Bill Chambers didn't answer 'im. He sat there as white as a sheet, and making such extraordinary faces that George was arf afraid of 'im.

"Anything wrong, Bill?" he ses at last.

Bill sat staring at 'im, and then all of a sudden he clapped 'is 'andkerchief to 'is mouth and, getting up from his chair, opened the door and rushed out. George Barstow thought at fust that he 'ad eaten pison for the sake o' ten shillings, but when 'e remembered that Bill Chambers 'ad got the most delikit stummick in Claybury he altered 'is mind.

The cat was better the next morning, but George Barstow had 'ad such a fright about it 'e wouldn't let it go out of 'is sight, and Joe Clark began to think that 'e would 'ave to wait longer for that property than 'e had thought, arter all. To 'ear 'im talk anybody'd ha' thought that 'e loved the cat. We didn't pay much attention to it up at the *Cauliflower* 'ere, except maybe to wink at 'im—a thing he couldn't a bear—but at 'ome, o' course, his young 'uns thought as everything he said was Gospel; and one day, coming 'ome from work, as he was passing George Barstow's he was paid out for his deceitfulness.

"I've wronged you, Joe Clark," ses George Barstow, coming to the door, "and I'm sorry for it."

"Oh!" ses Joe staring.

"Give that to your little Jimmy," ses George Barstow, giving 'im a shilling. "I've give 'im one, but I thought arterwards it wasn't enough."

"What for?" ses Joe, staring at 'im agin.

"For bringing my cat 'ome," ses George Barstow. "'Ow it got out I can't think, but I lost it for three hours, and I'd about given it up when your little Jimmy brought it to me in 'is arms. He's a fine little chap and 'e does you credit."

Joe Clark tried to speak, but he couldn't get a word out, and Henery Walker, wot 'ad just come up and 'eard wot passed, took hold of 'is arm and helped 'im home. He walked like a man in a dream, but arf-way he stopped and cut a stick from the hedge to take 'ome to little Jimmy.

[55]

He said the boy 'ad been asking him for a stick for some time, but up till then 'e'd always forgotten it.

At the end o' the fust year that cat was still alive, to everybody's surprise; but George Barstow took such care of it 'e never let it out of 'is sight. Every time 'e went out he took it with 'im in a hamper, and, to prevent its being pisoned, he paid Isaac Sawyer, who 'ad the biggest family in Claybury, sixpence a week to let one of 'is boys taste its milk before it had it.

The second year it was ill twice, but the horse-doctor that George Barstow got for it said that it was as 'ard as nails, and with care it might live to be twenty. He said that it wanted more fresh air and exercise; but when he 'eard 'ow George Barstow come by it he said that p'rhaps it would live longer indoors arter all.

At last one day, when George Barstow 'ad been living on the fat o' the land for nearly three years, that cat got out agin. George 'ad raised the front-room winder two or three inches to throw something outside, and, afore he knew wot was 'appening, the cat was outside and going up the road about twenty miles an hour.

George Barstow went arter it, but he might as well ha' tried to catch the wind. The cat was arf wild with joy at getting out again, and he couldn't get within arf a mile of it.

He stayed out all day without food or drink, follering it about until it came on dark, and then, o' course, he lost sight of it, and, hoping against 'ope that it would come home for its food, he went 'ome and waited for it. He sat up all night dozing in a chair in the front room with the door left open, but it was all no use; and arter thinking for a long time wot was best to do, he went out and told some o' the folks it was lost and offered a reward of five pounds for it.

You never saw such a hunt then in all your life. Nearly every man, woman, and child in Claybury left their work or school and went to try and earn that five pounds. By the arternoon George Barstow made it ten pounds provided the cat was brought 'ome safe and sound, and people as was too old to walk stood at their cottage doors to snap it up as it came by.

Joe Clark was hunting for it 'igh and low, and so was 'is wife and the boys. In fact, I b'lieve that everybody in Claybury excepting the parson and Bob Pretty was trying to get that ten pounds.

O' course, we could understand the parson—'is pride wouldn't let 'im; but a low, poaching, thieving rascal like Bob Pretty turning up 'is nose at ten pounds was more than we could make out. Even on the second day, when George Barstow made it ten pounds down and a shilling a week for a year besides, he didn't offer to stir; all he did was to try and make fun o' them as *was* looking for it.

"Have you looked everywhere you can think of for it, Bill?" he ses to Bill Chambers.

"Yes, I 'ave," ses Bill.

"Well, then, you want to look everywhere else," ses Bob Pretty. "I know where I should look if I wanted to find it."

"Why don't you find it, then?" ses Bill.

"'Cos I don't want to make mischief," ses Bob Pretty. "I don't want to be unneighbourly to Joe Clark by interfering at all."

"Not for all that money?" ses Bill.

"Not for fifty pounds," ses Bob Pretty; "you ought to know me better than that, Bill Chambers."

"It's my belief that you know more about where that cat is than you ought to," ses Joe Gubbins.

"You go on looking for it, Joe," ses Bob Pretty, grinning; "it's good exercise for you, and you've only lost two days' work."

[56]

"I'll give you arf a crown if you let me search your 'ouse, Bob," ses Bill Chambers, looking at 'im very 'ard.

"I couldn't do it at the price, Bill," ses Bob Pretty, shaking his 'ead. "I'm a pore man, but I'm very partikler who I 'ave come into my 'ouse."

O' course, everybody left off looking at once when they heard about Bob—not that they believed that he'd be such a fool as to keep the cat in his 'ouse; and that evening, as soon as it was dark, Joe Clark went round to see 'im.

"Don't tell me as that cat's found, Joe," ses Bob Pretty, as Joe opened the door.

"Not as I've 'eard of," said Joe, stepping inside. "I wanted to speak to you about it; the sooner it's found the better I shall be pleased."

"It does you credit, Joe Clark," ses Bob Pretty.

"It's my belief that it's dead," ses Joe, looking at 'im very 'ard; "but I want to make sure afore taking over the property."

Bob Pretty looked at 'im and then he gave a little cough. "Oh, you want it to be found dead," he ses. "Now, I wonder whether that cat's worth most dead or alive?"

Joe Clark coughed then. "Dead, I should think," he ses at last.

"George Barstow's just 'ad bills printed offering fifteen pounds for it," ses Bob Pretty.

"I'll give that or more when I come into the property," ses Joe Clark.

"There's nothing like ready-money, though, is there?" ses Bob.

"I'll promise it to you in writing, Bob," ses Joe, trembling.

"There's some things that don't look well in writing, Joe," ses Bob Pretty, considering; "besides, why should you promise it to *me*?"

"O' course, I meant if you found it," ses Joe.

"Well, I'll do my best, Joe," ses Bob Pretty; "and none of us can do no more than that, can they?"

They sat talking and argufying over it for over an hour, and twice Bob Pretty got up and said 'e was going to see whether George Barstow wouldn't offer more. By the time they parted they was as thick as thieves, and next morning Bob Pretty was wearing Joe Clark's watch and chain, and Mrs Pretty was up at Joe's 'ouse to see whether there was any of 'is furniture as she 'ad a fancy for.

She didn't seem to be able to make up 'er mind at fust between a chest o' drawers that 'ad belonged to Joe's mother and a grandfather clock. She walked from one to the other for about ten minutes, and then Bob, who'd come to 'elp her, told 'er to 'ave both.

"You're quite welcome," he ses; "ain't she, Joe?"

Joe Clark said "Yes," and arter he 'ad helped them carry 'em 'ome the Prettys went back and took the best bedstead to pieces, cos Bob said as it was easier to carry that way. Mrs Clark 'ad to go and sit down at the bottom o' the garden with the neck of 'er dress undone to give herself air, but when she saw the little Prettys each walking 'ome with one of 'er best chairs on their 'eads she got up and walked up and down like a mad thing.

"I'm sure I don't know where we are to put it all," ses Bob Pretty to Joe Gubbins, wot was looking on with other folks, "but Joe Clark is that generous he won't 'ear of our leaving any-thing."

"Has 'e gorn mad?" ses Bill Chambers, staring at 'im.

"Not as I knows on," ses Bob Pretty. "It's 'is good-'artedness, that's all. He feels sure that that cat's dead, and he'll 'ave George Barstow's cottage and furniture. I told 'im he'd better wait till he'd made sure, but 'e wouldn't."

Before they'd finished the Prettys 'ad picked that 'ouse as clean as a bone, and Joe Clark 'ad to go and get clean straw for his wife and children to sleep on; not that Mrs Clark 'ad any sleep that night, nor Joe neither.

Henery Walker was the fust to see what it really meant, and he went rushing off as fast as 'e could run to tell George Barstow. George couldn't believe 'im at fust, but when 'e did he swore that if a 'air of that cat's 'ead was harmed 'e'd 'ave the law o' Bob Pretty, and arter Henery Walker 'ad gone 'e walked round to tell 'im so.

"You're not yourself, George Barstow, else you wouldn't try and take away my character like that," ses Bob Pretty.

"Wot did Joe Clark give you all them things for?" ses George, pointing to the furniture.

"Took a fancy to me, I s'pose," ses Bob. "People do sometimes. There's something about me at times that makes 'em like me."

"He gave 'em to you to kill my cat," ses George Barstow. "It's plain enough for anybody to see."

Bob Pretty smiled. "I expect it'll turn up safe and sound one o' these days," he ses, "and then you'll come round and beg my pardon. P'r'aps—"

"P'r'aps wot?" ses George Barstow, arter waiting a bit.

"P'r'aps somebody 'as got it and is keeping it till you've drawed the fifteen pounds out o' the bank," ses Bob, looking at 'im very hard.

"I've taken it out o' the bank," ses George, starting; "if that cat's alive, Bob, and you've got it, there's the fifteen pounds the moment you 'and it over."

"Wot d'ye mean—me got it?" ses Bob Pretty. "You be careful o' my character."

"I mean if you know where it is," ses George Barstow trembling all over.

"I don't say I couldn't find it, if that's wot you mean," ses Bob. "I can gin'rally find things when I want to."

"You find me that cat, alive and well, and the money's yours, Bob," ses George, 'ardly able to speak, now that 'e fancied the cat was still alive.

Bob Pretty shook his 'ead. "No; that won't do," he ses. "S'pose I did 'ave the luck to find that pore animal, you'd say I'd had it all the time and refuse to pay."

"I swear I wouldn't, Bob," ses George Barstow, jumping up.

"Best thing you can do if you want me to try and find that cat," ses Bob Pretty, "is to give me the fifteen pounds now, and I'll go and look for it at once. I can't trust you, George Barstow."

"And I can't trust you," ses George Barstow.

"Very good," ses Bob, getting up; "there's no 'arm done. P'r'aps Joe Clark'll find the cat is dead and p'r'aps you'll find it's alive. It's all one to me."

George Barstow walked off 'ome, but he was in such a state o' mind 'e didn't know wot to do. Bob Pretty turning up 'is nose at fifteen pounds like that made 'im think that Joe Clark 'ad promised to pay 'im more if the cat was dead; and at last, arter worrying about if for a couple o' hours, 'e came up to this 'ere *Cauliflower* and offered Bob the fifteen pounds.

"Wot's this for?" ses Bob.

"For finding my cat," ses George.

"Look here," ses Bob, handing it back, "I've 'ad enough o' your insults; I don't know where your cat is."

"I mean for trying to find it, Bob," ses George Barstow.

"Oh, well, I don't mind that," ses Bob, taking it. "I'm a 'ard-working man, and I've got to be paid for my time; it's on'y fair to my wife and children. I'll start now."

He finished up 'is beer, and while the other chaps was telling George Barstow wot a fool he was Joe Clark slipped out arter Bob Pretty and began to call 'im all the names he could think of.

[58]

"Don't you worry," ses Bob; "the cat ain't found yet."

"Is it dead?" ses Joe Clark, 'ardly able to speak.

"'Ow should I know?" ses Bob; "that's wot I've got to try and find out. That's wot you gave me your furniture for, and wot George Barstow gave me the fifteen pounds for, ain't it? Now, don't you stop me now, 'cos I'm goin' to begin looking."

He started looking there and then, and for the next two or three days George Barstow and Joe Clark see 'im walking up and down with his 'ands in 'is pockets looking over garden fences and calling "Puss." He asked everybody 'e see whether they 'ad seen a white cat with one blue eye and one yaller one, and every time 'e came into the *Cauliflower* he put 'is 'ead over the bar and called "Puss," 'cos, as 'e said, it was as likely to be there as anywhere else.

It was about a week after the cat 'ad disappeared that George Barstow was standing at 'is door talking to Joe Clark, who was saying the cat must be dead and 'e wanted 'is property, when he sees a man coming up the road carrying a basket stop and speak to Bill Chambers. Just as 'e got near them an awful "miaow" come from the basket and George Barstow and Joe Clark started as if they'd been shot.

"He's found it!" shouts Bill Chambers, pointing to the man.

"It's been living with me over at Ling for a week pretty nearly," ses the man. "I tried to drive it away several times, not knowing that there was fifteen pounds offered for it."

George Barstow tried to take 'old of the basket.

Jack Russell and Persian, Frederick Rutherford (*Michael Parkin Fine Art Ltd*)

"I want that fifteen pounds fust," ses the man.

"That's on'y right and fair, George," ses Bob Pretty, who 'ad just come up. "You've got all the luck, mate. We've been hunting 'igh and low for that cat for a week."

Then George Barstow tried to explain to the man and call Bob Pretty names at the same time; but it was all no good. The man said it 'ad nothing to do with 'im wot he 'ad paid to Bob Pretty; and at last they fetched Policeman White over from Cudford, and George Barstow signed a paper to pay five shillings a week till the reward was paid.

George Barstow 'ad the cat for five years arter that, but he never let it get away agin. They got to like each other in time and died within a fortnight of each other, so Joe Clark got 'is property arter all.

Peter

~ ≈ ~

Marianne Moore

Strong and slippery, built for the midnight grass-party confronted by four cats,
   he sleeps his time away—the detached first claw on the foreleg, which corresponds
   to the thumb, retracted to its tip; the small tuft of fronds
     or katydid-legs above each eye, still numbering the units in each group;
     the shadbones regularly set about the mouth, to droop or rise

in unison like the porcupine's quills—motionless. He lets himself be flattened out by gravity, as it were a piece of seaweed tamed and weakened by
   exposure to the sun; compelled when extended, to lie
     stationary. Sleep is the result of his delusion that one must do as
     well as one can for oneself; sleep—epitome of what is to

him as to the average person, the end of life. Demonstrate on him how
   the lady caught the dangerous southern snake, placing a forked stick on either
   side of its innocuous neck; one need not try to stir
     him up; his prune-shaped head and alligator eyes are not a party to the
     joke. Lifted and handled, he may be dangled like an eel or set

up on the forearm like a mouse; his eyes bisected by pupils of a pin's
   width, are flickeringly exhibited, then covered up. May be? I should say
   might have been; when he has been got the better of in a
     dream—as in a fight with nature or with cats—we all know it. Profound sleep is
     not with him a fixed illusion. Springing about with froglike ac-

Contemplation, Henry Rogers (*Jellinek & Sampson*)

curacy, emitting jerky cries when taken in the hand, he is himself
    again; to sit caged by the rungs of a domestic chair would be unprofit-
    able—human. What is the good of hypocrisy? It
        is permissible to choose one's employment, to abandon the wire nail, the
        roly-poly, when it shows signs of being no longer a pleas-

ure, to score the adjacent magazine with a double line of strokes. He can
    talk, but insolently says nothing. What of it? When one is frank, one's very
    presence is a compliment. It is clear that he can see
        the virtue of naturalness, that he is one of those who do not regard
        the published fact as a surrender. As for the disposition

invariably to affront, an animal with claws wants to have to use
    them; that eel-like extension of trunk into tail is not an accident. To
    leap, to lengthen out, divide the air—to purloin, to pursue.
        To tell the hen: fly over the fence, go in the wrong way in your perturba-
        tion—this is life; to do less would be nothing but dishonesty.

The White and Black Dynasties

Théophile Gautier

(translated by Lady Chance)

A cat brought from Havana by Mademoiselle Aïta de la Penuela, a young Spanish artist whose studies of white angoras may still be seen gracing the printsellers' windows, produced the daintiest little kitten imaginable. It was just like a swan's-down powder-puff, and on account of its immaculate whiteness it received the name of Pierrot. When it grew big this was lengthened to Don Pierrot de Navarre as being more grandiose and majestic.

Don Pierrot, like all animals which are spoiled and made much of, developed a charming amiability of character. He shared the life of the household with all the pleasure which cats find

Cats on the Tiles, 1878

in the intimacy of the domestic hearth. Seated in his usual place near the fire, he really appeared to understand what was being said, and to take an interest in it.

His eyes followed the speakers, and from time to time he would utter little sounds, as though he too wanted to make remarks and give his opinion on literature, which was our usual topic of conversation. He was very fond of books, and when he found one open on a table he would lie on it, look at the page attentively, and turn over the leaves with his paw; then he would end by going to sleep, for all the world as if he were reading a fashionable novel.

Directly I took up a pen he would jump on my writing-desk and with deep attention watch the steel nib tracing black spider-legs on the expanse of white paper, and his head would turn each time I began a new line. Sometimes he tried to take part in the work, and would attempt to pull the pen out of my hand, no doubt in order to write himself, for he was an aesthetic cat, like Hoffman's Murr, and I strongly suspect him of having scribbled his memoirs at night on some house-top by the light of his phosphorescent eyes. Unfortunately these lucubrations have been lost.

Don Pierrot never went to bed until I came in. He waited for me inside the door, and as I entered the hall he would rub himself against my legs and arch his back, purring joyfully all the time. Then he proceeded to walk in front of me like a page, and if I had asked him, he would certainly have carried the candle for me. In this fashion he escorted me to my room and waited while I undressed; then he would jump on the bed, put his paws round my neck, rub noses with me, and lick me with his rasping little pink tongue, while giving vent to soft inarticulate cries, which clearly expressed how pleased he was to see me again. Then when his transports of affection had subsided, and the hour for repose had come, he would balance himself on the rail of the bedstead and sleep there like a bird perched on a bough. When I woke in the morning he would come and lie near me until it was time to get up. Twelve o'clock was the hour at which I was supposed to come in. On this subject Pierrot had all the notions of a concierge.

At that time we had instituted little evening gatherings among a few friends, and had formed a small society, which we called the Four Candles Club, the room in which we met being, as it happened, lit by four candles in silver candlesticks, which were placed at the corners of the table.

Sometimes the conversation became so lively that I forgot the time, at the risk of finding, like Cinderella, my carriage turned into a pumpkin and my coachman into a rat.

Pierrot waited for me several times until two o'clock in the morning, but in the end my conduct displeased him, and he went to bed without me. This mute protest against my innocent dissipation touched me so much that ever after I came home regularly at midnight. But it was a long time before Pierrot forgave me. He wanted to be sure that it was not a sham repentance; but when he was convinced of the sincerity of my conversion, he deigned to take me into favour again, and he resumed his nightly post in the entrance-hall.

To gain the friendship of a cat is not an easy thing. It is a philosophic, well-regulated, tranquil animal, a creature of habit and a lover of order and cleanliness. It does not give its affections indiscriminately. It will consent to be your friend if you are worthy of the honour, but it will not be your slave. With all its affection, it preserves its freedom of judgment, and it will not do anything for you which it considers unreasonable; but once it has given its love, what absolute confidence, what fidelity of affection! It will make itself the companion of your hours of work, of loneliness, or of sadness. It will lie the whole evening on your knee, purring and happy in your society, and leaving the company of creatures of its own kind to be with you. In vain the sound of caterwauling reverberates from the house-tops, inviting it to one of those cats' evening parties where essence of red-herring takes the place of tea. It will not be tempted, but continues to keep its vigil with you. If you put it down it climbs up again quickly, with a sort of crooning noise, which is like a gentle reproach. Sometimes, when seated in front of you, it gazes at you with such soft, melting eyes, such a human and caressing look, that you are almost awed, for it seems impossible that reason can be absent from it.

Don Pierrot had a companion of the same race as himself, and no less white. All the imaginable snowy comparisons it were possible to pile up would not suffice to give an idea of that immaculate fur, which would have made ermine look yellow.

I called her Seraphita, in memory of Balzac's Swedenborgian romance. The heroine of that wonderful story, when she climbed the snow peaks of the Falberg with Minna, never shone with a more pure white radiance. Seraphita had a dreamy and pensive character. She would lie motionless on a cushion for hours, not asleep, but with eyes fixed in rapt attention on scenes invisible to ordinary mortals.

Caresses were agreeable to her, but she responded to them with great reserve, and only to those of people whom she favoured with her esteem, which it was not easy to gain. She liked luxury, and it was always in the newest armchair or on the piece of furniture best calculated to show off her swan-like beauty, that she was to be found. Her toilette took an immense time. She would carefully smooth her entire coat every morning, and wash her face with her paw, and every hair on her body shone like new silver when brushed by her pink tongue. If anyone touched her she would immediately efface all traces of the contact, for she could not endure being ruffled. Her elegance and distinction gave one an idea of aristocratic birth, and among her own kind she must have been at least a duchess. She had a passion for scents. She would plunge her nose into bouquets, and nibble a perfumed handkerchief with little paroxysms of delight. She would walk about on the dressing-table sniffing the stoppers of the scent-bottles, and she would have loved to use the violet powder if she had been allowed.

Such was Seraphita, and never was a cat more worthy of a poetic name.

Don Pierrot de Navarre, being a native of Havana, needed a hot-house temperature. This he found indoors, but the house was surrounded by large gardens, divided up by palings through which a cat could easily slip, and planted with big trees in which hosts of birds twittered and sang; and sometimes Pierrot, taking advantage of an open door, would go out hunting of an evening and run over the dewy grass and flowers. He would then have to wait till morning to be let in again, for although he might come mewing under the windows, his appeal did not always wake the sleepers inside.

He had a delicate chest, and one colder night than usual he took a chill which soon developed into consumption. Poor Pierrot, after a year of coughing, became wasted and thin, and his coat, which formerly boasted such a snowy gloss, now put one in mind of the lustreless white of a shroud. His great limpid eyes looked enormous in his attentuated face. His pink nose had grown pale, and he would walk sadly along the sunny wall with slow steps, and watch the yellow autumn leaves whirling up in spirals. He looked as though he were reciting Millevoye's elegy.

There is nothing more touching than a sick animal; it submits to suffering with such gentle, pathetic resignation.

Everything possible was done to try and save Pierrot. He had a very clever doctor who sounded him and felt his pulse. He ordered him asses' milk, which the poor creature drank willingly enough out of his little china saucer. He lay for hours on my knee like the ghost of a sphinx, and I could feel the bones of his spine like the beads of a rosary under my fingers. He tried to respond to my caresses with a feeble purr which was like a death rattle.

When he was dying he lay panting on his side, but with a supreme effort he raised himself and came to me with dilated eyes in which there was a look of intense supplication. This look seemed to say: "Cannot you save me, you who are a man?" Then he staggered a short way with eyes already glazing, and fell down with such a lamentable cry, so full of despair and anguish, that I was pierced with silent horror.

He was buried at the bottom of the garden under a white rosebush which still marks his grave.

Seraphita died two or three years later of diphtheria, against which no science could prevail.

She rests not far from Pierrot. With her the white dynasty became extinct, but not the family. To this snow-white pair were born three kittens as black as ink.

Let him explain this mystery who can.

Just at that time Victor Hugo's *Misérables* was in great vogue, and the names of the characters in the novel were on everyone's lips. I called the two male kittens Enjolras and Gavroche, while the little female received the name of Eponine.

They were perfectly charming in their youth. I trained them like dogs to fetch and carry a bit of paper crumpled into a ball, which I threw for them. In time they learnt to fetch it from the tops of cupboards, from behind chests or from the bottom of tall vases, out of which they would pull it very cleverly with their paws. When they grew up they disdained such frivolous games, and acquired that calm philosophic temperament which is the true nature of cats.

To people landing in America in a slave colony all negroes are negroes, and indistinguishable

Olympia, Edouard Manet (*Musée du Louvre, Paris*)

from one another. In the same way, to careless eyes, three black cats are three black cats; but attentive observers make no such mistake. Animal physiognomy varies as much as that of men, and I could distinguish perfectly between those faces, all three as black as Harlequin's mask, and illuminated by emerald disks shot with gold.

Enjolras was by far the handsomest of the three. He was remarkable for his great leonine head and big ruff, his powerful shoulders, long back and splendid feathery tail. There was something theatrical about him, and he seemed to be always posing like a popular actor who knows he is being admired. His movements were slow, undulating and majestic. He put each foot down with as much circumspection as if he were walking on a table covered with Chinese bric-à-brac or Venetian glass. As to his character, he was by no means a stoic, and he showed a love of eating which that virtuous and sober young man, his namesake, would certainly have disapproved. Enjolras would undoubtedly have said to him, like the angel to Swedenborg: "You eat too much."

I humoured this gluttony, which was as amusing as a gastronomic monkey's, and Enjolras attained a size and weight seldom reached by the domestic cat. It occurred to me to have him shaved poodle-fashion, so as to give the finishing touch to his resemblance to a lion.

We left him his mane and a big tuft at the end of his tail, and I would not swear that we did not give him mutton-chop whiskers on his haunches like those Munito wore. Thus tricked out, it must be confessed he was much more like a Japanese monster than an African lion. Never was a more fantastic whim carved out of a living animal. His shaven skin took odd blue tints, which contrasted strangely with his black mane.

Gavroche, as though desirous of calling to mind his namesake in the novel, was a cat with an arch and crafty expression of countenance. He was smaller than Enjolras, and his movements were comically quick and brusque. In him absurb capers and ludicrous postures took the place of the banter and slang of the Parisian gamin. It must be confessed that Gavroche had vulgar tastes. He seized every possible occasion to leave the drawing-room in order to go and make up parties in the back-yard, or even in the street, with stray cats, "De naissance quelconque et de sang peu prouvé," in which doubtful company he completely forgot his dignity as cat of Havana, son of Don Pierrot de Navarre, grandee of Spain of the first order, and of the aristocratic and haughty Doña Seraphita.

Sometimes in his truant wanderings he picked up emaciated comrades, lean with hunger, and brought them to his plate of food to give them a treat in his good-natured, lordly way. The poor creatures, with ears laid back and watchful side-glances, in fear of being interrupted in their free meal by the broom of the housemaid, swallowed double, triple, and quadruple mouthfuls, and, like the famous dog Siete-Aguas (seven waters) of Spanish *posadas* (inns), they licked the plate as clean as if it had been washed and polished by one of Gerard Dow's or Mieris's Dutch housewives.

Seeing Gavroche's friends reminded me of a phrase which illustrates one of Gavarni's drawings, "Ils sont jolis les amis dont vous êtes susceptible d'aller avec!" ("Pretty kind of friends you like to associate with!")

But that only proved what a good heart Gavroche had, for he could easily have eaten all the food himself.

The cat named after the interesting Eponine was more delicate and slender than her brothers. Her nose was rather long, and her eyes slightly oblique, and green as those of Pallas Athene, to whom Homer always applied the epithet of γλαυκῶπις. Her nose was of velvety black, with the grain of a fine Périgord truffle; her whiskers were in a perpetual state of agitation, all of which gave her a peculiarly expressive countenance. Her superb black coat was always in

[66]

motion, and was watered and shot with shadowy markings. Never was there a more sensitive, nervous, electric animal. If one stroked her two or three times in the dark, blue sparks would fly crackling out of her fur.

Eponine attached herself particularly to me, like the Eponine of the novel to Marius, but I, being less taken up with Cosette than that handsome young man, could accept the affection of this gentle and devoted cat, who still shares the pleasures of my suburban retreat, and is the inseparable companion of my hours of work.

She comes running up when she hears the front-door bell, receives the visitors, conducts them to the drawing-room, talks to them—yes, talks to them—with little chirruping sounds, that do not in the least resemble the language cats use in talking to their own kind, but which simulate the articulate speech of man. What does she say? She says in the clearest way, "Will you be good enough to wait till monsieur comes down? Please look at the pictures, or chat with me in the meantime, if that will amuse you." Then when I come in she discreetly retires to an armchair or a corner of the piano, like a well-bred animal who knows what is correct in good society. Pretty little Eponine gave so many proofs of intelligence, good disposition and sociability, that by common consent she was raised to the dignity of a *person*, for it was quite evident that she was possessed of higher reasoning power than mere instinct. This dignity conferred on her the privilege of eating at table like a person instead of out of a saucer in a corner of the room like an animal.

So Eponine had a chair next to me at breakfast and dinner, but on account of her small size she was allowed to rest her two front paws on the edge of the table. Her place was laid, without spoon or fork, but she had her glass. She went right through dinner dish by dish, from soup to dessert, waiting for her turn to be helped, and behaving with such propriety and nice manners as one would like to see in many children. She made her appearance at the first sound of the bell, and on going into the dining-room one found her already in her place, sitting up in her chair with her paws resting on the edge of the table-cloth, and seeming to offer you her little face to kiss, like a well-brought-up little girl who is affectionately polite towards her parents and elders.

As one finds flaws in diamonds, spots on the sun, and shadows on perfection itself, so Eponine, it must be confessed, had a passion for fish. She shared this in common with all other cats. Contrary to the Latin proverb, "Catus amat pisces, sed non vult tingere plantas," she would willingly have dipped her paw into the water if by so doing she could have pulled out a trout or a young carp. She became nearly frantic over fish, and, like a child who is filled with the expectation of dessert, she sometimes rebelled at her soup when she knew (from previous investigations in the kitchen) that fish was coming. When this happened she was not helped, and I would say to her coldly: "Mademoiselle, a person who is not hungry for soup cannot be hungry for fish," and the dish would be pitilessly carried away from under her nose. Convinced that matters were serious, greedy Eponine would swallow her soup in all haste, down to the last drop, polishing off the last crumb of bread or bit of macaroni, and would then turn round and look at me with pride, like someone who has conscientiously done his duty. She was then given her portion, which she consumed with great satisfaction, and after tasting of every dish in turn, she would finish up by drinking a third of a glass of water.

When I am expecting friends to dinner Eponine knows there is going to be a party before she sees the guests. She looks at her place, and if she sees a knife and fork by her plate she decamps at once and seats herself on a music-stool, which is her refuge on these occasions.

Let those who deny reasoning powers to animals explain if they can this little fact, apparently so simple, but which contains a whole series of inductions. From the presence near her

In the Pantry, A. Roland Knight (*Michael Parkin Fine Art Ltd*)

plate of those implements which man alone can use, this observant and reflective cat concludes that she will have to give up her place for that day to a guest, and promptly proceeds to do so. She never makes a mistake; but when she knows the visitor well she climbs on his knee and tries to coax a tit-bit out of him by her pretty caressing ways.

Cat

Alan Brownjohn

Sometimes I am an unseen
marmalade cat, the friendliest colour,
making off through a window without permission,
pacing along a broken-glass wall to the greenhouse,
jumping down with a soft, four-pawed thump,

finding two inches open of the creaking door
with the loose brass handle,
slipping impossibly in,
flattening my fur at the hush and touch of the sudden warm air,
avoiding the tiled gutter of slow green water,
skirting the potted nests of tetchy cactuses,
and sitting with my tail flicked
skilfully underneath me, to sniff
the azaleas   the azaleas   the azaleas.

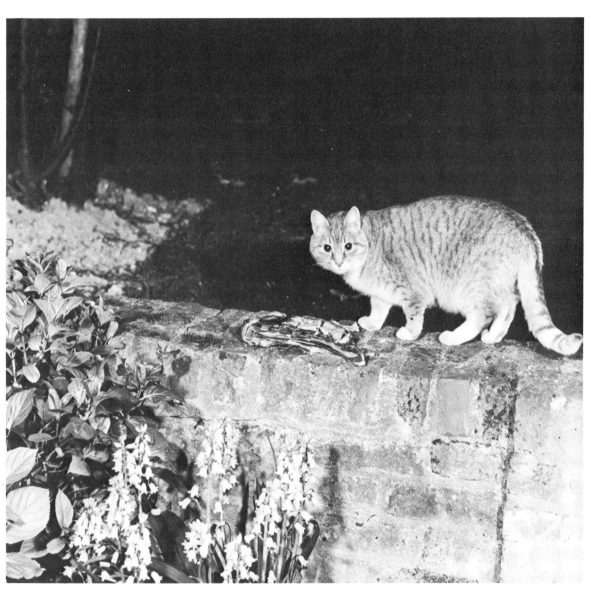

Cat at Foxes' Bait, photo D. N. Dalton (*Natural History Photographic Agency*)

Rhymes for the Nursery (1839)

Pussy-cat Mew

Pussy-cat Mew jumped over a coal,
And in her best petticoat burnt a great hole.
Pussy-cat Mew shall have no more milk
Till she has mended her gown of silk.

Kitty: How to Treat Her

I like little Pussy, her coat is so warm,
And if I don't hurt her she'll do me no harm;
So I'll not pull her tail, nor drive her away,
But Pussy and I very gently will play.

The Graham Children, William Hogarth (*Tate Gallery, London*)

Ten Little Mice

Ten little mice sat down to spin;
Pussy passed by, and just looked in,
"What are you doing, my jolly ten?"
"We're making coats for gentlemen."
"Shall I come in and cut your threads?"
"No! No! Mistress Pussy—you'd bite off our heads."

FROM
The Cat by the Fire

Leigh Hunt

Poor Pussy! she looks up at us again, as if she thanked us for those vindications of dinner; and symbolically gives a twist of a yawn and a lick of her whiskers. Now she proceeds to clean herself all over, having a just sense of the demands of her elegant person—beginning judiciously with her paws, and fetching amazing tongues at her hind-hips. Anon, she scratches her neck with a foot of rapid delight, leaning her head towards it, and shutting her eyes, half to accommodate the action of the skin, and half to enjoy the luxury. She then rewards her paws with a few more touches; look at the action of her head and neck, how pleasing it is, the ears pointed forward, and the neck gently arching to and fro. Finally, she gives a sneeze, and another twist of mouth and whiskers, and then, curling her tail towards her front claws, settles herself on her hind quarters, in an attitude of bland meditation . . .

She is a sprightly cat, hardly past her youth; so, happening to move the fringe of the rug a little with our foot, she darts out a paw, and begins plucking it and inquiring into the matter, as if it were a challenge to play, or something lively enough to be eaten. What a graceful action of that foot of hers, between delicacy and petulance!—combining something of a thrust out, a beat and a scratch. There seems even something of a little bit of fear in it, as if just enough to provoke her courage, and give her the excitement of a sense of hazard. We remember being much amused with seeing a kitten manifestly making a series of experiments upon the patience of its mother— trying how far the latter would put up with positive bites and thumps. The kitten ran at her every moment, gave her a knock or a bite of the tail; then ran back again, to recommence the assault. The mother sat looking at her, as if betwixt tolerance and admiration, to see how far the spirit of the family was inherited by her sprightly offspring. At length, however, the "little Pickle" presumed too far, and the mother, lifting up her paw, and meeting her at the very nick of the moment, gave her one of the most unsophisticated boxes on the ear we ever beheld. It sent her rolling half over the room, and made her come to the most ludicrous pause, with the oddest little look of premature and wincing meditation . . .

[71]

At the Zoo

Mark Twain

In the great Zoological Gardens [of Marseille] we found specimens of all the animals the world produces, I think . . . The boon companion of the colossal elephant was a common cat! This cat had a fashion of climbing up the elephant's hind legs, and roosting on his back. She would sit up there, with her paws curved under her breast, and sleep in the sun half the afternoon. It used to annoy the elephant at first and he would reach up and take her down, but she would go aft and climb up again. She persisted until she finally conquered the elephant's prejudices, and now they are inseparable friends. The cat plays about her comrade's forefeet or his trunk often, until dogs approach, and then she goes aloft out of danger. The elephant has annihilated several dogs lately, that pressed his companion too closely.

The Family Cat

Roy Fuller

This cat was bought upon the day
That marked the Japanese defeat;
He was anonymous and gay,
But timorous and not discreet.

Although three years have gone, he shows
Fresh sides of his uneven mind:
To us—fond, lenient—he grows
Still more eccentric and defined.

He is a grey, white-chested cat,
And barred with black along the grey;
Not large, and the reverse of fat,
His profile good from either way.

The poet buys especial fish,
Which is made ready by his wife;
The poet's son holds out the dish:
They thus maintain the creature's life.

It's not his anniversary
Alone that's his significance:
In any case mortality
May not be thought of in his presence.

For brief as are our lives, more brief
Exist. Our stroking hides the bones,
Which none the less cry out in grief
Beneath the mocking, loving tones.

Cat, Gwen John (*Tate Gallery, London*)

The Ballad of Tough Tom

Paul Gallico

That's right!
Those are tufts of my fur you're looking at.
What about it?
You don't see the other cat, do you?
What are a few hairs
Compared to an ear?
I didn't get the whole of his off
Because by then he was already heading south,
Having had enough.
But it was eminently satisfactory.
My name is Tough Tom,
And I am King of the Car Park.
When the sun shines
It warms the hoods of the cars for us.
We like that.
We lie on them.
Sometimes we get chased because
We leave footmarks on the cars,
But most of the time nobody bothers,
We have our own crowd that comes here
To sun.
But I say who does and who doesn't.
See?
Because I'm King of the Car Park.
So one day this stranger walks up and says,
"What's your name?"
So I says, "Tough Tom
And I'm King of the Car Park. What's yours?"
And he says, "Tough Charlie, and I guess
You ain't King of the Car Park anymore."
"Oh, I get it," I says, "You're looking for a little action."
"How did you guess?" says Tough Charlie.
I'm measuring him up in the meantime

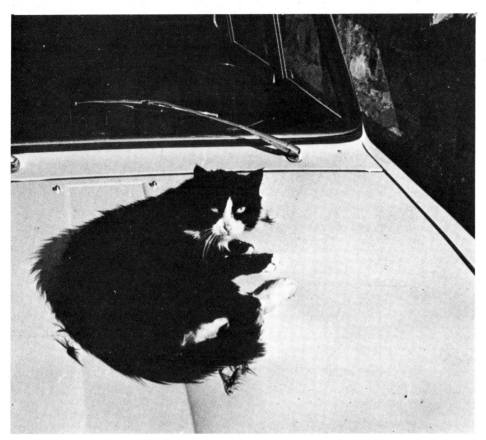

Tough Tom, photo Osamu Nishikawa

And he's a lot of cat.
Yellow and white.
Yellow is a colour I ain't partial to.
And although I wasn't looking for trouble that morning,
Like now by being King of the Car Park,
It was up to me to oblige. So I says,
"Shall we dispense with the preliminaries?
See now, like the growling
And the fluffing
And the humping up
And the exchange of insults?"
Waste of time
When you know you're going to mix.
"Okay by me," says Tough Charlie, "Let's go!"
And he's up and onto me, leading with his right.
Oh boy, a sucker punch.
But I guess I'm a little dopey,
Lying out in that hot sun,

On that warm hood
And maybe he's got a half a pound on me as well.
So I'm on my back before I know it,
And he just misses getting my eye out.
Tough Charlie he was all right.
I give my left on the end of his nose
And try a roll-over
But he's too smart for that
And goes for my eye again, only this time
I'm waiting for it.
He don't get the eye,
But I get his ear.
Brother!
We're all over that car,
Down on the ground,
And underneath,
And back up on top again,
With the gang sitting around
Waiting to see
Who is the King of the Car Park.
He gives me the raking kick

Fighting Cats, (Museo del Prado, Madrid)

With the back legs.
That's when I lost all that fur
You see about.
But I've still got that ear,
And it's starting to come away.
Tough Tom and Tough Charlie
And the battle of the Car Park!
They'll sing about that one on the tiles
For many a night.
So I guess maybe Tough Charlie thinks it over,
That with only one ear
He ain't gonna do so good anymore
With the broads, and he says,
"Okay, so I was wrong. Leggo!
You're still King of the Car Park."
So I had to laugh, and he's off
With what's left of his ear.
That's the story.
So now for a little clean-up.
I'm still Tough Tom,
King of the Car Park.

FROM
Jubilate Agno

Christopher Smart

For I will consider my Cat Jeoffrey.
For he is the servant of the Living God, duly and daily serving him.
For at the First glance of the glory of God in the East he worships in his way.
For this is done by wreathing his body seven times round with elegant quickness.
For then he leaps up to catch the musk, which is the blessing of God upon his prayer.
For he rolls upon prank to work it in.
For having done duty and received blessing he begins to consider himself.
For this he performs in ten degrees.
For first he looks upon his fore-paws to see if they are clean.
For secondly he kicks up behind to clear away there.
For thirdly he works it upon stretch with the fore-paws extended.
For fourthly he sharpens his paws by wood.

For fifthly he washes himself.

For sixthly he rolls upon wash.

For Seventhly he fleas himself, that he may not be interrupted upon the beat.

For Eighthly he rubs himself against a post.

For Ninthly he looks up for his instructions.

For Tenthly he goes in quest of food.

For having consider'd God and himself he will consider his neighbour.

For if he meets another cat he will kiss her in kindness.

For when he takes his prey he plays with it to give it a chance.

For one mouse in seven escapes by his dallying.

For when his day's work is done his business more properly begins.

For he keeps the Lord's watch in the night against the adversary.

For he counteracts the powers of darkness by his electrical skin & and glaring eyes.

For he counteracts the Devil, who is death, by brisking about the life.

For in his morning orisons he loves the sun and the sun loves him.

For he is of the tribe of Tiger.

For the Cherub Cat is a term of the Angel Tiger.

For he has the subtlety and hissing of a serpent, which in goodness he suppresses.

For he will not do destruction, if he is well fed, neither will he spit without provocation.

For he purrs in thankfulness, when God tells him he's a good Cat.

Two Boys with Pets, unknown American artist (*Philadelphia Museum of Art, The Edgar William and Bernice Chrysler Garbisch Collection*)

For he is an instrument for the children to learn benevolence upon.

For every house is incomplete without him and a blessing is lacking in the spirit.

For the Lord commanded Moses concerning the cats at the departure of the Children of
Israel from Egypt.

For every family had one cat at least in the bag.

For the English Cats are the best in Europe.

For he is the cleanest in the use of his fore-paws of any quadrupede.

For the dexterity of his defence is an instance of the love of God to him exceedingly.

For he is the quickest to his mark of any creature.

For he is tenacious of his point.

For he is a mixture of gravity and waggery.

For he knows that God is his Saviour.

For there is nothing sweeter than his peace when at rest.

For there is nothing brisker than his life in motion.

For he is of the Lord's poor and so indeed is he called by benevolence perpetually—Poor
Jeoffrey! poor Jeoffrey! the rat has bit thy throat.

For I bless the name of the Lord Jesus that Jeoffrey is better.

For the divine spirit comes about his body to sustain it in complete cat.

For his tongue is exceedingly pure so that it has in purity what it wants in music.

For he is docile and can learn certain things.

For he can set up with gravity which is patience upon approbation.

For he can fetch and carry, which is patience in employment.

For he can jump over a stick which is patience upon proof positive.

For he can spraggle upon waggle at the word of command.

For he can jump from an eminence into his master's bosom.

For he can catch the cork and toss it again.

For he is hated by the hypocrite and miser.

For the former is afraid of detection.

For the latter refuses the charge.

For he camels his back to bear the first notion of business.

For he is good to think on, if a man would express himself neatly.

For he made a great figure in Egypt for his signal services.

For he killed the Ichneumon-rat very pernicious by land.

For his ears are so acute that they sting again.

For from this proceeds the passing quickness of his attention.

For by stroking of him I have found out electricity.

For I perceived God's light upon him both wax and fire.

For the Electrical fire is the spiritual substance, which God sends from heaven to sustain the
bodies both of man and beast.

For God has blessed him in the variety of his movements.

For, tho he cannot fly, he is an excellent clamberer.

For his motions upon the face of the earth are more than any other quadrupede.

For he can tread to all the measures upon the music.

For he can swim for life.

For he can creep.

A Letter to his Daughter

Theodore Roosevelt

White House, 6th January 1903

Dear Kermit,

We felt very melancholy after you and Ted left and the house seemed empty and lonely. But it was the greatest possible comfort to feel that you both really have enjoyed school and are both doing well there.

Tom Quartz is certainly the cunningest kitten I have ever seen. He is always playing pranks on Jack and I get very nervous lest Jack should grow too irritated. The other evening they were both in the library—Jack sleeping before the fire—Tom Quartz scampering about, an exceedingly playful little creature—which is about what he is. He would race across the floor, then jump upon the curtain or play with the tassel. Suddenly he spied Jack and galloped up to him. Jack, looking exceedingly sullen and shame-faced, jumped out of the way and got upon the sofa and around the table, and Tom Quartz instantly jumped upon him again. Jack suddenly shifted to the other sofa, where Tom Quartz again went after him. Then Jack started for the door, while Tom made a rapid turn under the sofa and around the table and just as Jack reached the door leaped on his hind-quarters. Jack bounded forward and away and the two went tandem out of the room— Jack not co-operating at all; and about five minutes afterwards Tom Quartz stalked solemnly back.

Another evening, the next Speaker of the House, Mr Cannon, an exceedingly solemn, elderly gentleman with chin whiskers, who certainly does not look to be of playful nature, came to call upon me. He is a great friend of mine, and we sat talking over what our policies for the session should be until about eleven o'clock and when he went away I accompanied him to the head of the stairs. He had gone about half-way down when Tom Quartz strolled by, his tail erect and very fluffy. He spied Mr Cannon going down the stairs, jumped to the conclusion that he was a playmate escaping, and raced after him, suddenly grasping him by the leg the way he does Archie and Quentin when they play hide and seek with him; then loosening his hold he tore downstairs ahead of Mr Cannon, who eyed him with an iron calm and not one particle of surprise . . .

The Girl with Cat, Alfred Dehodencq (*Private Collection*)

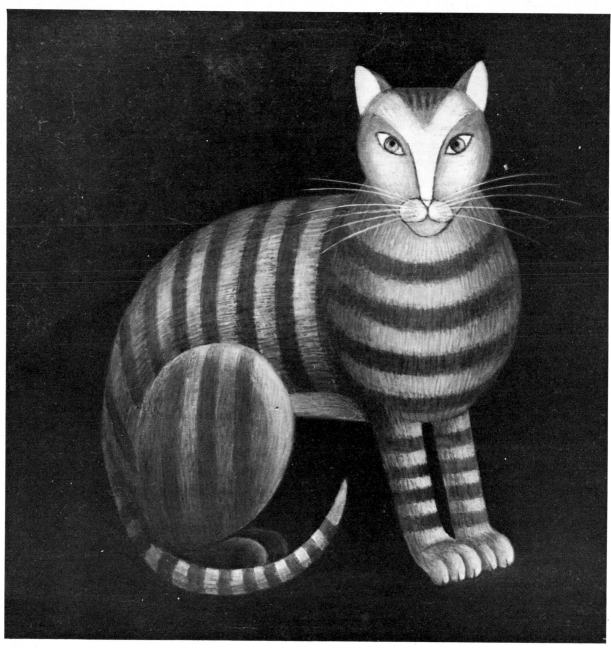

Striped Cat, Walter Bell Currie (*Crane Kalman Gallery*)

IV

～ Cat's Love ～

Esther's Tomcat

Ted Hughes

Daylong this tomcat lies stretched flat
As an old rough mat, no mouth and no eyes.
Continual wars and wives are what
Have tattered his ears and battered his head.

Like a bundle of old rope and iron
Sleeps till blue dusk. Then reappear
His eyes, green as ringstones: he yawns wide red,
Fangs fine as a lady's needle and bright.

A tomcat sprang at a mounted knight,
Locked round his neck like a trap of hooks
While the knight rode fighting its clawing and bite.
After hundreds of years the stain's there

On the stone where he fell, dead of the tom:
That was at Barnborough. The tomcat still
Grallochs odd dogs on the quiet,
Will take the head clean off your simple pullet,

Is unkillable. From the dog's fury,
From gunshot fired point-blank he brings
His skin whole, and whole
From owlish moons of bekittenings

Among ashcans. He leaps and lightly
Walks upon sleep, his mind on the moon.
Nightly over the round world of men,
Over the roofs go his eyes and outcry.

Cat and Lady

Paul Verlaine
(translated by Arthur Symons)

They were at play, she and her cat,
And it was marvellous to mark
The white paw and the white hand pat
Each other in the deepening dark.

Woman with a Cat, Edouard Manet (*Tate Gallery, London*)

The stealthy little lady hid
Under her mittens' silken sheath
Her deadly agate nails that thrid
The silk-like dagger points of death.

The cat purred primly and drew in
Her claws that were of steel filed thin:
The devil was in it all the same.

And in the boudoir, while a shout
Of laughter in the air rang out,
Four sparks of phosphor shone like flame.

Nature Notes: Cats

Louis MacNeice

Incorrigible, uncommitted,
They leavened the long flat hours of my childhood,
Subtle, the opposite of dogs,
And, unlike dogs, capable
Of flirting, falling, and yawning anywhere,
Like women who want no contract
But going their own way
Make the way of their lovers lighter.

The Jealous One

Giles Gordon

They stood at the threshold, the lintel above their heads, like the blade of a guillotine. Hand in
hand, they would have been stunned as they waited there, had the blade fallen, as they felt each

other, as they looked at the faces that looked at them. But their end was not thus ordained at this moment in time. Their new life had just begun.

They entered the room in which the reception was being held (the room that was to become the bedroom, if not the bridal chamber), she in white, he in—mainly—black.

Ninety-seven faces were turned towards the door, not expectantly, confidently. Some of them forgot to hold their smiles. All were bored, most without knowing it.

Her lips were smeared red, cherry wet. Not a hair on his usually unruly scalp was out of place. They smiled—at those who smiled at them, at the room itself, at the pictures on the wall, at the mirror (if they could see themselves in it!), at the memory and anticipation of the bed. Now they were inside the room, they smiled at each other. Edward. Angela.

From a place known to him but not to them, the cat smiled.

"Please . . . Kiss each other. Yes, like that. Just like that. Thank you. Hold it."

Flash. A premonition of lightning. Someone looked up at the ceiling, that had become sky, that had become blue. An aircraft glittered past the bright sun. They rubbed their eyes. Inside the room again.

"Thank you, Mr and Mrs . . . em . . . yes, Mr and Mrs. Ha!"

"A family group. We must have a family group."

The individuals were assembled, pushed together, smiled (again) without being persuaded to do so.

Flash. A premonition of blinding. Staggering about in the darkness, unable to see the sun that beat down so sweatily.

The sixteen people in the portrait tumbled apart, moved away from each other, avoiding the honey pot. Laughter reverberated as the two pairs of lips touched again. Peck, peck. Snap. Already they had memories to treasure, to store up and misinterpret. Their mouths glued together. Gobble, gobble. Held. After the shot.

Champagne glasses were raised in the direction of the heavens; hard, dry, curranty wedding cake was washed down.

The cat was almost sick, would have been had Edward not forgotten to feed him that morning, before he left the house in such a rush amidst so much clatter and turmoil. The beginning of the end, the first time in four years he'd forgotten to feed him.

There were eighty—two hundred—people in the room. Parents, in-laws, aunts, cousins, nephews, a step-brother, bridesmaids, sisters, colleagues from work, a grand-parent, a school-friend not encountered for six years, a best man (a brother), vague distant relatives not seen or even spoken of previously, Angela's ballet mistress (her legs were muscular but no varicose veins apparent to the naked eye), Edward's sometime stamp collector friend. The I-thee-wed man, imagining himself a bishop, was present in the flesh but not in the spirit.

"Hold it."

Another caught-in-the-act job.

The laughter ceased. Sssh . . . Flash. The laughter built up again. The cat nipped an ankle, but when he-who-was-nipped looked down there was no cat to be seen.

Shaking hands, eating, smiling, kissing, crying, drinking, oh the happy (unconsummated) scene, knew him (her) when he (she) was so high, so low. Always been pretty (ugly), has Angela. I know someone who'll be very jealous of him. Very jealous. Maternal tears into a scented, embroidered handkerchief. The cut of the cake, cutting the cake. Flash. Again. And again. His hand up her dress, no one (else) noticing, all eyes upon her face, the veil thrown back, abused. Her lips open, thrust apart, her face at the moment of orgasm (the camera doesn't lie), the cake popped in. A contraceptive pill, a wafer. Wired corks ricocheting across the room,

Woman with Cat, Alexander Archipenko (*Kunstmuseum Düsseldorf*)

hitting walls and ceiling, raining down on the guests like bullets. The happy couple.

The remark was not recorded, then or now, but someone said: Funny, a cat at a wedding.

Others noticed Edward's cat, those who knew him, knew his cat. The cat, surprisingly, believed that no one—least of all Edward, which was true—had noticed him.

And they cried, those who wore their emotions near to their eyes, after he was dead.

Rat-tat-tat-tat.

One bullet. In the forehead, in the temple. Goliath felled by David. Or some such comparison.

And he fell over in slow fast slow motion.

"A priest!"

The vicar had departed. He'd drunk the couple's health, stuffed his mouth with crumbling, flaky white icing, and left after ten minutes, the bishopric no nearer. Others to administer to, services to officiate at. You know? I do apologise. Beautiful wedding, thank you vicar.

His words were a little odd, as was his presence, as they'd been married at a registry office. He'd come along for history's sake.

Not a Catholic. Neither, obviously, were they. A bun in the ovary (orifice).

Edward checked the cake, the champagne, the guests, his wife. And they cried after he was dead. Fell over slow, slow, faster. Stop. No more movement. A pin didn't drop.

Then they began to crowd around, Angela alone not near him, having fled the scene of carnage and tragedy for what reason we can but speculate. A heartless girl, you think? Or an over-sensitive child?

Rat-tat-tat-tat.

They turned round, the guests, their heads moving as if they belonged to an immaculately drilled opera chorus. A generation ago, most of them might have crossed themselves. He fell, fell, fell. Who could have. Loved by everyone. Such a promising career. No enemies. Knew his father. Mafia? IRA? On his wedding day!

The cat stood by the door, a revolver in his left hand.

Puss in Boots, Gustave Doré

(Impossible. Cats have four legs, four paws; no hands. They do not stand on two legs, except occasionally when leaning against an upright surface, when they desire to reach a height a few feet or more above them. If a cat is said to stand on two legs, there must be an error. The animal seen thus cannot have been a cat.)

The revolver smoked, smouldered. Was hot. The cat tilted the barrel towards his green, oriental eyes; looked up the barrel. There was no bullet to be seen, only smoke coiling out of the muzzle.

The cat looked up from the revolver, at the wedding guests. His ego was wounded: no one was looking at him. They all looked at Edward, at the body.

"Do not panic," said the cat, in a loud, toneless voice.

(Impossible. Cats do not speak. Their vocal chords are different in kind from those of humans. I never thought, never imagined, that the day would come when we would be able to understand each other, so-called cats and so-called humans.)

"Do not panic," said the cat, and the figures caught in the act of bending over the recumbent (now dead) body of the groom turned—as if caught with their trousers round their ankles—to look at him from whom emanated the voice, the words. They could see nobody, nobody again in the act of making a public utterance.

There were three people bending over the corpse. His bride of less than an hour (presumably having had second thoughts about where her duty lay); Dr Cole, a physician friend on the groom's side of the family; and Angela's mother.

"There's nobody there," said Mrs Ankarah (Angela's mama; her present husband—not at the wedding—not being Angela's father).

"There's nobody there," repeated Mrs Ankarah, having risen to her feet, and peered short-sightedly towards the entrance of the room where stood (only) the cat. Everyone in the room looked towards the door, as that was where the voice undoubtedly spoke from, except for the dead Edward.

Such fools, thought the cat. They don't even notice a pussy when he's holding a smoking revolver.

The cat waved the revolver, determined to attract attention. Would he have to kill them all before they saw him? And then who would notice?

Dr Cole was bending over the recent Edward, undoing buttons. He had undone so many, yet there still seemed more to undo than there had been at the beginning. Why was he trying to expose what he was trying to expose? Had he not felt the heart, known it was not beating?

Angela was weeping, shaking her head, willing the mascara to run. The tragic heroine, the wronged bride, the lustful widow—of all this she still knew nothing. She would have the photographs.

"There's nobody there," repeated Mrs Ankarah.

As unintelligent as she looks, thought the cat. He slunk forward, towards the family pietà attended by family doctor. A path was cleared for him, the funeral guests moved aside to let him through without giving the impression that they were moving, for him or for anyone. He was grateful for this, as it added to his dignity. He *could* have gone through their legs, but he'd had to have crawled.

He stood next to the body. And spoke:

"I knew Edward more . . . intimately than any of you did. He had no right to marry Sonia."

A few murmurs. Now they saw who was speaking, who was holding a revolver. It had ceased to smoke.

"Angela," said her mother. "We thought of Sonia but decided against."

"Mother!" screamed and sobbed the wronged bride, if screaming and sobbing can be accomplished simultaneously.

"What's in a name?" said the cat, shrugging his shoulders. "I'm called just pussy, and I get by."

There was an indrawing of breath throughout the room. Outrageous. Appalling. Wicked. Scandalous. Should be put down. This moment. Dangerous animal.

The mourners moved away from the body, perhaps (but unlikely, as Edward was dead; though nobody as yet had said so) to allow it to breathe, perhaps afraid of the cat. The cat stood, one eye on the hundred, two hundred people in what had been, would be again, the centre of the house, the room of the bed; the other on his Edward.

Lazarus-like, if Edward desired sufficiently to return to life, thought the cat, to prove that his heart hadn't ceased to breathe, this was his moment. The cat willed him to live. But there was one provision; and Edward knew it; and knew that the cat knew that he knew. He would have to choose—Angela, or pussy.

Until this moment (he was thinking in death), Edward hadn't realised what the choice was; that there *was* a choice. Now he understood everything, certainly why his beloved pussy had shot him. How thoughtless he'd been, how insensitive. But why not both? He could make Angela understand, he was sure of that. She was a pliable girl, and she could hardly feel challenged by a cat. But pussy wouldn't accept her—under any circumstances? Under none—that was clear.

Edward thought on the past, on the four . . . idyllic years he and pussy had had. But what had happened had happened, pussy was behind him, Angela was in front. Couldn't the three of them live together, love together? He had no desire to hurt the cat, to cause him pain. No, Edward finally decided, he couldn't make the choice. It was too much for him. It was unfair of pussy to expect him to be able to make it. He would have to remain dead.

Rat-tat-tat-tat.

And he wheeled over in slow fast slow motion, grasping at what he'd never clutched. The icing of the wedding cake disintegrated in a cascade of powder, lifted into the air. The guests began coughing and choking. His body brushed the floor lightly, as if trying to protect the carpet. There was no blood to be seen.

The guests began talking to each other again, exchanging news of relatives some of them had thought long since dead. They resumed gorging themselves on the fare provided, downing glass after glass of champagne, to drown the memory of anything unpleasant or distasteful that might have happened.

Edward—still on the ground; on the ground not to rise again—crawled towards the door of the room on all fours, uncertain whether it was entrance or exit, the beginning or end. No one in the room appeared to notice his progress, except for the cat. Of course, except for the cat.

"I've phoned for an ambulance," Dr Cole whispered to Mrs Ankarah; and she would have communicated the news to Edward's parents had they been alive. "Told the ambulance people there was nothing for them to do, except take the body away."

Mrs Ankarah nodded gratefully, and gulped. As long as Angela didn't think of a nunnery, or something extreme like that.

The cat watched the man crawling, looked down at him. Towards the door, towards the exit, about to leave his own wedding.

And they cried after he was dead.

As he died.

On the Prowl, Henry Rogers (*Jellinek & Sampson*)

Rat-tat-tat-tat.

I, Edward Anigram, dearly beloved husband of Angela Ankarah Anigram, leave all my worldly possessions to my wife, and the recesses of my mind to pussy (my cat), who has been my sensual adviser and consort for so many seasons. As I draw up this will, I sincerely wish it were I who were dying, not he . . .

But it is, Edward, it is, thought pussy; and I have killed you.

No human being would have done it, only an insensitive, jealous animal.

The cat donned dark glasses, so that no one could see his eyes. All those people might be mourning Edward's end; what did they imagine that he, Edward's lover, felt? No one could see if he had an expression of remorse, or of sorrow, on his visage. Angela wondered, and he sensed her thought and was grateful, whether he regretted what he had done; did he care; could he feel; did he realise that . . . she had loved, that she still loved Edward? Why didn't he stick to catching mice or rats, or if he must sparrows? Though certainly not budgies, which Edward had told her he'd once done when some child's pet bird had been released temporarily from its gilded prison, then forgotten until too late.

The cat decided to instil in what passed for Angela's mind the idea that he, pussy, had loved Edward, and allow her mind to play on that concept.

Someone, not Dr Cole, dialled 999. Ambulance—*and* police. Then you have to make two separate calls, Mrs. Yes, to the same number.

Someone else dialled 999.

[93]

The cat purred, but no one listened. He'd triumphed in adversity. They were all tense, neurotic, bewildered, the guests. They'd come to a wedding, found themselves witnesses to a murder of a peculiar kind. Witnesses, yet none of them had seen it happen. There'd been a cat, some thought with a gun, but the idea was . . . ridiculous.

"Murder?" said a would-be husband's of Angela's. "Don't you think murder's rather a strong word?"

Rat-tat-tat-tat.

The angle from immediately inside the door to where Edward and Angela stood, tickling each other's clammy palms.

"Look, there's my beloved pussy", said Edward to his bride.

But he didn't say that, he hadn't referred to the cat at all. He might not have existed. What would my life be without Edward, thought the cat, and though the intention presumably was—Edward hadn't confided—that he and Mrs Edward would live in the house together, the three of them, well, it wouldn't be the same. He knew they'd do things together, the two of them, have a relationship, maybe even a child, who would tweak him, pull his tail, worse still his whiskers. Such a ghastly domestic scene must be pre-empted, thought pussy as bride and groom arrived at their reception. Better to do it now than when the heart (his, hers) grows fond.

The cat understood certain things about man, not others. Had Edward even alluded to him once, given him a credit, he wouldn't then have asked to be centre of the stage. A backroom boy, he'd have been satisfied. If Edward was fit to wed Angela today, the relationship that had existed between him and pussy had to be important. If no one else knew this, he and Edward did; and now Angela knew.

Rat-tat-tat-tat.

Edward lay down and died. Angela ran from the room, her mouth open in a soundless scream that encompassed her whole life up to that moment. Out of the room, across the hall, into the bedroom . . . But the bedroom was the room in which the guests were, where Edward was. The cat rose up in front of her. Larger, larger, larger. As he stretched out two paws towards her, to hold her body, she . . . fainted.

Edward and he knew things, between each other, intuitively. It wasn't as if they had talked together, had understood each other's minds. Nothing so advanced as that. Empathy, maybe; logic, no. Therefore.

His eyes were closed at the moment the bullet hit him. Of course he had known it was coming. He'd known his affair with the cat could only be ended by his marrying somebody; and he loved Angela.

And they cried after he was dead.

The ambulance men removed the body, on a stretcher, and covered it with a red blanket as if to compensate for the lack of blood shed.

The police officers took a few notes, asked a few questions, removed the revolver, holding it on a cloth so as not to smudge the paw-prints.

Thank you all for your cooperation. Desperately sorry. The worst case of its kind I've come across. Thank you. Try to forget it.

Hands shaken, heads bowed. The caterers cleared up the dead bottles, the cardboard plates, the crumbs, the remaining sandwiches, biscuits, melted ice-cream, jelly, the accoutrements of a wedding.

Angela couldn't leave.

"Come along, my poor love," said her mother, when everyone else had gone.

She shook her head, her face damp and dirty, her mind confused, her world in turmoil.

"I'm staying."

Her mother tried to pull her by the elbow, Angela drew herself away.

"I want to stay."

"Not here. On your own. In this house."

"In our house. In my house."

She smiled at her mother, stood close beside her.

"Mother, please leave me here for a little while. On my own. I want to be alone. To think. Just to be here."

"Very well. But don't be long; not too long."

Mrs Ankarah smiled at her daughter, Angela smiled back. She watched her mother walk through the house, stood for a few seconds following her progress out of the front door, down the garden path. Her mother didn't look back, and Angela closed the front door.

She stood, leaning against the inside of the door for half a minute, her eyes closed. Then she began to walk towards the bedroom.

The cat was standing there, waiting for her. She knew he would be. It was what she wanted, what she had learned to want.

She smiled at pussy. He was purring.

"Angela," he said.

"Edward," she said.

the song of mehitabel

Don Marquis

—the song is written by archy who is a cockroach who writes free verse on an office typewriter; mehitabel is an alley cat—

this is the song of mehitabel
of mehitabel the alley cat
as i wrote you before boss
mehitabel is a believer
in the pythagorean
theory of the transmigration
of the souls and she claims
that formerly her spirit
was incarnated in the body
of cleopatra

that was a long time ago
and one must not be
surprised if mehitabel
has forgotten some of her
more regal habits

i have had my ups and downs
but wotthehell wotthehell
yesterday sceptres and crowns
fried oysters and velvet gowns
and today i herd with bums
but wotthehell wotthehell

Feline, Alan Durst (*Tate Gallery, London*)

i wake the world from sleep
as i caper and sing and leap
when i sing my wild free tune
wotthehell wotthehell
under the blear eyed moon
i am pelted with cast off shoon
but wotthehell wotthehell

do you think that i would change
my present freedom to range
for a castle or moated grange
wotthehell wotthehell
cage me and i d go frantic
my life is so romantic
capricious and corybantic
and i m toujours gai toujours gai

i know that i am bound
for a journey down the sound
in the midst of a refuse mound
but wotthehell wotthehell
oh i should worry and fret
death and i will coquette
there s a dance in the old dame yet
toujours gai toujours gai

i once was an innocent kit
wotthehell wotthehell
with a ribbon my neck to fit
and bells tied onto it
o wotthehell wotthehell
but a maltese cat came by
with a come hither look in his eye
and a song that soared to the sky
and wotthehell wotthehell
and i followed adown the street
the pad of his rhythmical feet
o permit me again to repeat
wotthehell wotthehell

my youth i shall never forget
but there s nothing i really regret
wotthehell wotthehell
there s a dance in the old dame yet
toujours gai toujours gai

[97]

the things that i had not ought to
i do because i ve gotto
wotthehell wotthehell
and i end with my favourite motto
toujours gai toujours gai

boss sometimes i think
that our friend mehitabel
is a trifle too gay

                    archy

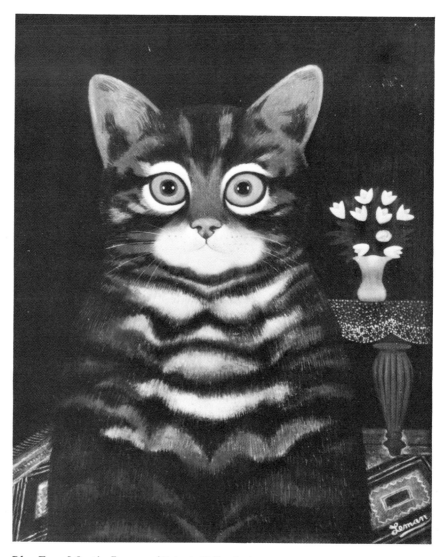

Blue Eyes, Martin Leman (*Private Collection*)

mehitabel s extensive past

Don Marquis

mehitabel the cat claims that
she has a human soul
also and has transmigrated
from body to body and **it**
may be so boss you
remember i told you she accused
herself of being cleopatra once i
asked her about antony

anthony who she asked me are
you thinking of that
song about rowley and gammon and
spinach heigho for anthony rowley

no i said mark antony the
great roman the friend of
caesar surely cleopatra you
remember j caesar

listen archy she said i
have been so many different
people in my time and met
so many prominent gentlemen i
wont lie to you or stall i
do get my dates mixed sometimes
think of how much i have had a
chance to forget and i have
always made a point of not
carrying grudges over
from one life to the next archy

i have been
used something fierce in my time but
i am no bum sport archy

i am a free spirit archy i
look on myself as being
quite a romantic character oh the
queens i have been and the
swell feeds i have ate
a cockroach which you are
and a poet which you used to be
archy couldn t understand
my feelings at having come
down to this i have
had bids to elegant feeds where poets
and cockroaches would
neither one be mentioned without a
laugh archy i have had
adventures but i
have never been an adventuress
one life up and the next life
down archy but always a lady
through it all and a
good mixer too always the
life of the party archy but never
anything vulgar always free footed
archy never tied down to
a job or housework yes looking
back on it all i can say is
i had some romantic
lives and some elegant times i
have seen better days archy but
what is the use of kicking kid its
all in the game like a gentleman
friend of mine used to say
toujours gai kid toujours gai he
was an elegant cat he used
to be a poet himself and he made up
some elegant poetry about me and him

lets hear it i said and
mehitabel recited

persian pussy from over the sea
demure and lazy and smug and fat
none of your ribbons and bells for me
ours is the zest of the alley cat
over the roofs from flat to flat
we prance with capers corybantic
what though a boot should break a slat
mehitabel us for the life romantic

[100]

we would rather be rowdy and guant and free
and dine on a diet of roach and rat

roach i said what do you
mean roach interrupting mehitabel
yes roach she said that s the
way my boy friend made it up
i climbed in amongst the typewriter
keys for she had an excited
look in her eyes go on mehitabel i
said feeling safer and she
resumed her elocution

we would rather be rowdy and guant and free
and dine on a diet of roach and rat
than slaves to a tame society
ours is the zest of the alley cat

Cat Eating a Bird, Pablo Picasso (*Photographie Giraudon*)

fish heads freedom a frozen sprat
dug from the gutter with digits frantic
is better than bores and a fireside mat
mehitabel us for the life romantic
when the pendant moon in the leafless tree
clings and sways like a golden bat
i sing its light and my love for thee
ours is the zest of the alley cat
missiles around us fall rat a tat tat
but our shadows leap in a ribald antic
as over the fences the world cries scat
mehitabel us for the life romantic

persian princess i don t care that
for your pedigree traced by scribes pedantic
our is the zest of the alley cat
mehitabel us for the life romantic

aint that high brow stuff
archy i always remembered it
but he was an elegant gent
even if he was a highbrow and a
regular bohemian archy him and
me went aboard a canal boat
one day and he got his head into
a pitcher of cream and couldn t get
it out and fell overboard
he come up once before he
drowned toujours gai kid he
gurgled and then sank for ever that
was always his words archy toujours
gai kid toujours gai i
have known some swell gents
in my time dearie

                    archy

Lady Chasing Cat with Parrot, Kangra, *c.* 1810 (*Victoria and Albert Museum. Crown Copyright*)

Miss Brummell, Thomas Gainsborough (*Iveagh Bequest, Kenwood*)

My cat and i

Roger McGough

Girls are simply the prettiest things
My cat and i believe
And we're always saddened
When it's time for them to leave

Portrait of Pierre Loti, Henri Rousseau (*Kunsthaus Zürich*)

[103]

We watch them titivating
(that often takes a while)
And though they keep us waiting
My cat & i just smile

We like to see them to the door
Say how sad it couldn't last
Then my cat and i go back inside
And talk about the past.

To My Lord Buckhurst, Very Young, Playing with a Cat

Matthew Prior

The am'rous Youth, whose tender Breast
Was by his darling Cat possest,
Obtain'd of VENUS his Desire,
Howe'er irregular his Fire:
Nature the Pow'r of Love obey'd:
The Cat became a blushing Maid;
And, on the happy Change, the Boy
Imploy'd his Wonder and his Joy.

Take care, O beauteous Child, take care,
Lest Thou prefer so rash a Pray'r:
Nor vainly hope, the Queen of Love
Will e'er thy Fav'rite's Charms improve.
O quickly from her Shrine retreat;
Or tremble for thy Darling's Fate.

The Queen of Love, who soon will see
Her own ADONIS live in Thee,
Will lightly her first Loss deplore;
Will easily forgive the Boar:
Her Eyes with Tears no more will flow;
With jealous Rage her Breast will glow:
And on her tabby Rival's Face
She deep will mark her new Disgrace.

Chalk sketch, Léopold Louis Boilly (*Achenbach Foundation, California Palace of the Legion of Honor, San Francisco*)

What Did You Do There?

Harvey Jacobs

Marvin Carton's affair with Eileen Vincent-Norman was complicated by a cat named Humphrey, a white cat that grew to enormous size after he was fixed.

When Eileen Vincent-Norman told Marvin Carton that Humphrey was "altered" Marvin

Carton was not only surprised, he was angry. The whole idea was outrageous. On the other hand, after the surgery, Humphrey stopped leaping onto Marvin Carton's back at embarrassing moments. And Marvin Carton no longer thought the great fluffy cat a threat to his privates. So, the action that first seemed to reveal a strange and dark part of Eileen Vincent-Norman's personality (fixer of cats), ultimately proved to be good common sense.

With Humphrey's new behaviour, a contented withdrawal, an occasional desire for a scratch on the belly, in contrast with a former malevolence and terrible energy, Marvin Carton found it easier and less complicated to lie naked with Eileen Vincent-Norman. He lost the need to keep alert for frenzied furry attack and to repress more rage when Eileen Vincent-Norman interpreted those feline assaults as "cute" or "darling". Also he was less worried about having to carry paw marks on his sensitive back, or God knows where else, and explain those to his wife.

Even the cat syndrome that seemed so important to Eileen Vincent-Norman annoyed Marvin Carton less. The box of litter and cat-do in the bathroom, the bowls of fish, the rubber toys shaped like mice—all were easier to take after the traumatic operation. Marvin Carton was, in fact, freer to appreciate Eileen Vincent-Norman's delicious young beauty and sensual response. For a girl so young—she was hardly twenty—she knew so much, knew it with a flesh knowledge that was really splendid and amazing. Marvin Carton, just past forty, felt her move against him and was renewed, sparks of human nourishment leapt between them, it was all very good from the first and better still since Humphrey's visit to the veterinarian.

One problem remained, it had been there all along, but since the undoing of Humphrey's equipment seemed to grow worse. The cat shed snowfalls of hair. Everything in Eileen Vincent-Norman's apartment was prey to cat-hair, white, long cat-hair. In the winter of their affair steam heat and dry air filled her apartment with static electricity that made the hairs stand up and fly toward Marvin Carton's clothes. He was a magnet.

"You're getting prematurely grey," was a joke of Eileen Vincent-Norman's as she ran over his business suit with a fuzz remover, or a band-aid, or a damp turkish towel.

Yes, winter was the worst time since Marvin Carton's suits were mostly blue. The hairs clung and covered his pants and jacket like graffiti. And because he always visited Eileen Vincent-Norman after work, he was always dressed in conservative clothes. He longed for summer and a new pale wardrobe—wash and wear garments of white or seersucker that would camouflage the cat hairs like soldiers in the bush.

The prevalence of Humphrey's shed hairs disturbed three aspects of Marvin Carton's affair. First, he could no longer simply rip off his clothes in abandon and leave them on the carpet while he carried Eileen Vincent-Norman to the bedroom or sofa. She liked it when he did that because of the spontaneity and because of Marvin Carton's easy disregard for the crease in his $200 Cardin pants. Now if he did anything but pause to hang his clothes they came up saturated with white. Even the hangers had cat-hair on them, impossible though that seemed. Second, because of the sheddings, Eileen Vincent-Norman had to de-fuzz Marvin Carton as he was about to leave for home. His pleasure in leaving her naked, sleepy, drowsing while he departed like a phantom after filling her with warmth and honey, was ruined by the neccessary ritual act of having a roller of sticky tape run over him collar to cuffs. The abrupt return to reality not only broke the mood but led to practical conversation as to the ultimate dimensions of their sparkling relationship, how long it would last, whether it was right or wrong. Once Eileen Vincent-Norman asked Marvin Carton to stay a moment and help balance her check-book. He did, sitting at a bridge-table, and had to be rolled again because the table was full of cat. The third and most annoying problem was Marvin Carton's wife and daughter. They both had terrific eyes, better than 20–20, a joy to the optometrist. If there was a crumb in the house they

The Family, Gustaaf De Smet (*Musées royaux des Beaux-Arts, Brussels*)

could see it in darkness. Cat-hairs, white long cat-hairs on a blue suit, made them blink as if they were staring into sun. And despite Eileen Vincent-Norman's care, and Marvin Carton's pickings on the way home, a few of Humphrey's hairs always remained. It was impossible to get them all.

"Where have you been sitting?"

"Nowhere."

"Look, Daddy. Another one. Whee!"

"Marvin, where *have* you been sitting?"

"Now how the hell do I answer a question like that?"

"Daddy said hell. God will bite you."

"Where does she learn things like that?"

"Look, Marvin. Under your arm."

"This city is filthy."

Because of all this, Marvin Carton had to change the rhythm of his visits to Eileen Vincent-Norman. He came later to her apartment and he left later. By leaving later he could get home after his child was sleeping and his wife was weary. He could slide through the darkened apartment, into the bathroom, and de-fuzz himself of leftovers. The leftovers, two or three white strands each visit, he dropped cleverly into an unused laundry cabinet. If he threw them into the sink or the john they could form a clogging knot. Some plumber would come when the water rose and say something like, "Did you drown a horse down here, lady?" to his wife. But the laundry cabinet, a metal built-in thing, was never used except to store old work-clothes. Some day, alone, Marvin Carton could clean out the multitudes of cat hairs and dispose of them quietly and efficiently.

Meanwhile, because of his later visits, he could see less of Eileen Vincent-Norman. To find an excuse for working until midnight was much more complicated than finding an excuse for coming home at ten. Visitors from out-of-town would not come in more than a few times a month. Eileen Vincent-Norman was very understanding. She never made trouble. She liked the affair with married Marvin Carton and was not possessive beyond the normal moments of clutch and hold. She did not want a permanent alliance, why should she, he was old enough to be her father. Marvin Carton adored the girl as well he might. She was worth the guilt feelings, the deceptions, the lies, even the cat-hairs. When he began to see less of her it was, curiously, at a time when he wanted to see more of her. And Marvin Carton did not want Eileen Vincent-Norman to think for a minute that he was growing tired of her. She was beautiful, nubile, intelligent, and superb in bed. Their sex woke him to new energy.

"I feel like a kid," he would say to the immortal young girl. "I feel like I came over a ridge and discovered the Pacific."

"Thank you," Eileen Vincent-Norman would say.

She even reminded him when it was time to go home. If he told her they had guests coming she set her alarm radio so he would be unpressured. And setting the alarm she always turned the radio to semi-classical music, not hard rock. And left ten minutes for rolling the tape over Marvin Carton's blue knit. She only asked about his wife occasionally, and then, her questions were never personal. That was a girl to be cherished, God knows, to be defended and treasured.

At home one night, near four in the morning, Marvin Carton's wife woke him.

"I heard something," she said.

"From upstairs," Marvin Carton said, yawning.

"A meow."

"From outside."

"From the bathroom."

"From the what?"

"I must have beeen dreaming."

They went back to sleep.

It happened again the next night. Marvin Carton had been with Eileen Vincent-Norman earlier, and had made love with her three times. That was a lot after a full business day and he was depleted beyond his vitamin E. He hit the pillow and slept hard, dreaming of an elevator that went up and down a thousand times. His wife shook him awake and said, "There is a meowing in the bathroom."

Marvin Carton got up, went to investigate. Only a few hours before he had added a few strands of Humphrey's errant hair to the collection in the laundry cabinet. Now here he was checking out a mystical "meow", fighting to keep conscious.

"There's nothing meowing. Lord, it must be plumbing. Or a neighbour's pussycat."

"I suppose."

Marvin Carton got back into bed, dreamed again, and was blasted awake by a cat shriek.

"From the yard. They must be mating."

"It came from the bathroom."

Their daughter was wakened too and already in the bathroom "doing her business".

"It's making me nervous," said Marvin Carton's wife.

"Ah."

Then their daughter came out, hiking up her pajamas, holding a kitten.

"Mommy, Daddy, a pussy."

The parents looked.

"The pussy came out of the laundry house," their daughter said. "Can I keep him?"

In the morning, Marvin Carton took two Librium. His wife decided the cat had somehow crawled in through a window and gotten into the cabinet, though she marvelled at its resourcefulness. Their daughter was assured she could keep the cat, it was time she had a pet other than a mangy turtle that said Welcome to Miami Beach on its back.

Marvin Carton continued the normal routine of his life. He continued to use the laundry cabinet to store Humphrey's hairs, which may have been a mistake since a month later another white pussycat wandered into the bedroom and climbed into the bed where he and his wife slept bottom to bottom.

"It's really some kind of miracle," his wife said. "What a darling."

It was decided to keep the second cat as a companion to the first. This meant more litter, more fish, more water in the cup on the kitchen floor. And as the cats grew, it meant more fixing, a stiff bill from the veterinarian (he used the same veterinarian as Eileen Vincent-Norman who recommended him highly), subsequent larger cats and shedding of their own.

He never told Eileen Vincent-Norman that the operation was for his cats. He told her he had a friend whose cats needed the full treatment. He never mentioned the cats to Eileen Vincent-Norman in any shape, size or form. There was surely a spooky force at work, and he didn't want to upset the girl. Besides he was ashamed of himself. It had occurred to him that the cats, spinoffs of Humphrey, were somehow sent to do harm to his wife and daughter. Messengers from Eileen Vincent-Norman to dispose of competition so that she could have Marvin Carton for her own. That was ridiculous. The cats were nothing but loving. Besides, Eileen Vincent-Norman told Marvin Carton she was dating an accountant and that it might turn serious. There was never any doubt that if that happened their affair would turn to warm friendship and nothing more.

The upshot of two cats at home and one cat at Eileen Vincent-Norman's was that Marvin Carton's business suits were gardens of fuzz. He was forever having tape run over him or pulling at himself. Even his ivory summer suit and subsequent seersucker held the hairs. And the warm months passed too quickly. Before he knew it his wife told him,

"Marvin, you can't wear those light things any more. It's practically October."

Now, back to darker fabrics, the cat-hair explosion was definitely a plague to be contended with. His boss had mentioned "good grooming" more than once. The hairs became harder to remove. And one night, in the shower, washing Eileen Vincent-Norman's delicious love with

Cat and Mirror, photo Lynwood M. Chace (*Frank W. Lane*)

Ivory soap, he noticed cat-hairs on his very body. And they were hard to get rid of. They hurt when he went at them. And left welts. So he stopped trying.

Six months later, Marvin Carton stopped wearing clothes. He was totally covered with a lush, Siamese growth, so clothes were redundant.

"You'd better comb yourself more carefully," his wife said. And he did. He spent inordinate amounts of time combing and brushing and licking his pelt.

At work, his boss was forced to level with him.

"Marvin, I don't give a damn about a man's dress. But upstairs they do. And you're an executive. They don't want an abominable snowman walking around. You'll get a fine severance check. And you're vested in the pension plan. Of course, upon termination, you'll have to furnish your own Blue Cross."

So Marvin Carton was unemployed. It never rains, it pours. Eileen Vincent-Norman fell in love with her accountant and told Marvin Carton that they could no longer sleep together. They had slept together little enough since his hair grew. He tickled and Eileen Vincent-Norman was turned off by her own giggles. Humphrey, on the other hand was very friendly. Marvin Carton played with him on the floor, chasing a pimpled rubber ball and crunching cellophane from cigarette packages.

After a session with Humphrey he had to go home and play with his own cats, East and West they were named. It was quite exhausting. And Marvin Carton was concerned because he had heard his wife on the telephone with the veterinarian recommended by Eileen Vincent-Norman. They talked in whispers.

"I'm taking you downtown for some shots and a trim," his wife said to Marvin Carton.

"Where?"

"To the vet. To the nice vet. He's promised to give you a collar and a bell if you behave yourself."

"Shots and a trim? Is that all?"

"Certainly, dear."

"A collar and a bell?"

"If you behave yourself."

"Nothing more? Right?"

"Right. Would I kid you?"

"No."

"The same vet we used before?"

"The same one. You'll feel at home with him, won't you?"

"Sure. Sure. No problem."

"I've got some nice chicken parts for you."

"Expensive chicken parts?"

"Yes. And champagne."

"How come? Why the celebration?"

' No special reason," his wife said.

"No special reason?"

"What reason would there be?"

"No reason."

"That's what I said, dear."

Marvin Carton jumped at a fly. There was something going on. He couldn't put his paw on it.

Woman Holding a White Pussy Cat, Sylvia Emmons (*Crane Kalman Gallery*)

V

～ Cat's Magic ～

Cat-Goddesses

Robert Graves

A perverse habit of cat-goddesses—
Even the blackest of them, black as coals
Save for a new moon blazing on each breast,
With coral tongues and beryl eyes like lamps,
Long-leggèd, pacing three by three in nines—
This obstinate habit is to yield themselves
In verisimilar love-ecstasies,
To tatter-eared and slinking alley-toms
No less below the common run of cats
Than they above it; which they do for spite,
To provoke jealousy—not the least abashed
By such gross-headed, rabbit-coloured litters
As soon they shall be happy to desert.

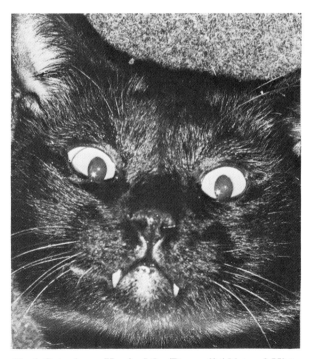

Black Cat, photo Kevin MacDonnell (*Natural History Photographic Agency*)

[115]

Broomsticks

Walter de la Mare

Miss Chauncey's cat, Sam, had been with her many years before she noticed anything unusual, anything *disturbing*, in his conduct. Like most cats who live under the same roof with but one or two humans, he had always been more sagacious than cats of a common household. He had learned Miss Chauncey's ways. He acted, that is, as nearly like a small mortal dressed up in a hairy coat as one could expect a cat to act. He was what is called an "intelligent" cat.

But though Sam had learned much from Miss Chauncey, I am bound to say that Miss Chauncey had learned very little from Sam. She was a kind indulgent mistress; she could sew, and cook, and crochet, and make a bed, and read and write and cipher a little. And when she was a girl she used to sing "Kathleen Mavourneen" to the piano. Sam, of course, could do nothing of this kind.

But then, Miss Chauncey could no more have caught and killed a mouse or a blackbird with her five naked fingers than she could have been Pope of Rome. Nor could she run up a six-foot brick wall, or leap clean from the hearth-mat in her parlour on to the shelf of her chimney-piece without disturbing a single ornament, or even tinkle one crystal glass-drop against another. Unlike Sam, she could not find her way in the dark, or by her sense of smell; or keep in good health by merely nibbling grass in the garden. If, moreover, as a little girl she had been held up by her feet and hands two or three feet above the ground and then dropped, she would have at once fallen plump on her back, whereas when Sam was only a three-month-old, he could have managed to twist clean about in the air in twelve inches and come down on his four feet as firm as a table.

While Sam, then, had learned a good deal from Miss Chauncey, she had learned nothing from him. And even if she had been willing to be taught, it is doubtful if she would ever have proved even a promising pupil. What is more, she knew much less about Sam than he knew about his mistress—until, at least, that afternoon when she was doing her hair in the glass. And then she could hardly believe her own eyes. It was a moment that completely changed her views about Sam—and nothing after that experience was ever quite the same again.

Sam had always been a fine upstanding creature, his fur jet-black and silky, his eyes a lambent green, even in sunshine, and at night a-glow like green topazes. He was now full seven years of age, and had an unusually powerful miaou. Living as he did quite alone with Miss Chauncey at Post Houses, it was natural that he should become her constant companion. For Post Houses was a singularly solitary house, standing almost in the middle of Haggurdsdon Moor, just where two wandering byways cross each other like the half-closed blades of a pair of shears or scissors.

It was a mile and a half from its nearest neighbour, Mr Cullings, the carrier; and yet another quarter of a mile from the village of Haggurdsdon. Its roads were extremely ancient. They had been sheep-tracks long before the Romans came to England and had cut *their* roads from shore to shore. But for many years past few travellers or carts or even sheep with their shepherd came Miss Chauncey's way. You could have gazed from her windows for hours together, even on a summer's day, without seeing so much as a tinker's barrow or a gipsy's van.

Post Houses, too, was perhaps the ugliest house there ever was. Its four corners stood straight up on the moor like a house of nursery bricks. From its flat roof on a clear day the eye could see for miles across the moor, Mr Cullings' cottage being out of sight in a shallow hollow. It had belonged to Miss Chauncey's ancestors for numbers of generations. Many people in Haggurds-don indeed called it Chauncey's. And though in a great wind it was almost as full of noises as an organ, though it was a cold barn in winter and though another branch of the family had as far back as the seventies gone to live in the Isle of Wight, Miss Chauncey still remained faithful to its four walls. In fact she loved the ugly old place, for she had lived in it ever since she was a little girl with knickerbockers showing under her skirts and pale-blue ribbon shoulder knots.

This fact alone made Sam's conduct the more reprehensible, for never cat had kinder mistress. Miss Chauncey herself was now about sixty years of age—fifty-three years older than Sam. She was five foot ten-and-a-half inches in height. On weekdays she wore black alpaca, and on Sundays a watered silk. Her large round steel spectacles straddling across her high nose gave her

Young Woman Holding a Black Cat, Gwen John (*Tate Gallery, London*)

[117]

a look of being keen as well as cold. But truly she was neither. For even so stupid a man as Mr Cullings could take her in over the cartage charge of a parcel—just by looking tired or sighing as he glanced at his rough-haired, knock-kneed mare. And there was the warmest of hearts under her stiff bodice.

Being so far from the village, milk and cream were a little difficult, of course. But Miss Chauncey could deny Sam nothing—in reason. She paid a whole sixpence a week to a little girl called Susan Ard who brought these dainties from the nearest farm. They were dainties indeed, for though the grasses on Haggurdsdon Moor were of dark sour green, the cows that grazed on it gave an uncommonly rich milk, and Sam flourished on it. Mr Cullings called once a week on his round, and had a standing order to bring with him a few sprats or fresh herrings, or any other toothsome fish that was in season. Miss Chauncey would not even withold her purse from expensive whitebait, if no other cheaper fish were procurable. And Mr Cullings would eye Sam fawning about his cartwheel, or gloating up at his dish, and say, "'Ee be a queer animal, shure enough; 'ee be a wunnerful queer animal, 'ee be."

As for Miss Chauncey herself, she was a niggardly eater, though much attached to her tea. She made her own bread and biscuits. On Saturday a butcher-boy drove up in a striped apron. Besides which she was a wonderful manager. Her cupboards were full of homemade jams and bottled fruits and dried herbs—everything of that kind, for Post Houses had a nice long strip of garden behind it, surrounded by a high old yellow brick wall.

Quite early in life Sam, of course, had learned to know his mealtime—though how he "told" it was known only to himself, for he never appeared even to glance at the face of the grandfather's clock on the staircase. He was punctual, particularly in his toilet, and a prodigious sleeper. He had learned to pull down the latch of the back door, if, in the months when an open window was not to be found, he wished to go out. Indeed at last he preferred the latch. He never slept on Miss Chauncey's patchwork quilt, unless his own had been placed over it. He was particular almost to a foppish degree in his habits, and he was no thief. He had a mew on one note to show when he wanted something to eat; a mew a semitone or two higher if he wanted drink (that is, cold water, for which he had a great taste); and yet another mew—gentle and sustained—when he wished, so to speak, to converse with his mistress.

Not, of course, that the creature talked *English*, but he liked to sit up on one chair by the fireside, especially in the kitchen—for he was no born parlour-cat—and to look up at the glinting glasses of Miss Chauncey's spectacles, and then down awhile at the fire-flames (drawing his claws in and out as he did so, and purring the while), almost as if he might be preaching a sermon, or reciting a poem.

But this was in the happy days when all seemed well. This was in the days when Miss Chauncey's mind was innocent of all doubts and suspicions. Like others of his kind, too, Sam delighted to lie in the window and idly watch the birds in the apple-trees—tits and bullfinches and dunnocks—or to crouch over a mouse-hole for hours together. Such were his amusements (for he never ate his mice) while Miss Chauncey with cap and broom, duster and dishclout, went about her housework. But he also had a way of examining things in which cats are not generally interested. He as good as told Miss Chauncey one afternoon that a hole was coming in her parlour carpet. For he walked to and fro and back and forth with his tail up, until she attended to him. And he certainly warned her, with a yelp like an Amazonian monkey, when a red-hot coal had set her kitchen mat on fire.

He would lie or sit with his whiskers to the North before noonday, and due South afterwards. In general his manners were perfection. But occasionally when she called him, his face would appear to knot itself into a frown—at any rate to assume a low sullen look, as if he expostulated

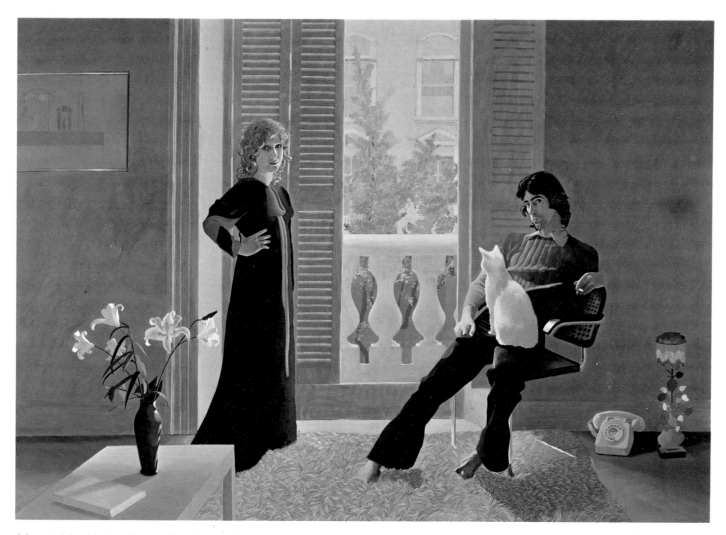

Mr and Mrs Clark and Percy, David Hockney (*Tate Gallery, London*)

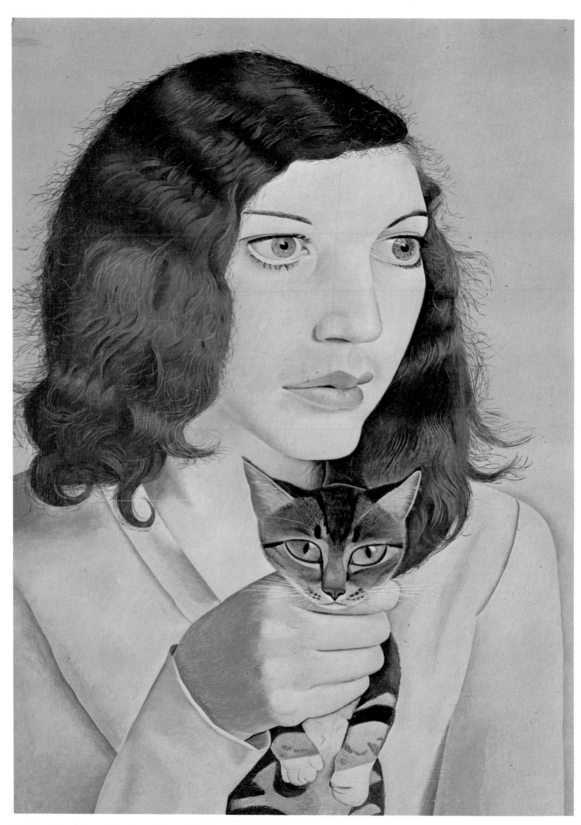

Girl with a Kitten, Lucian Freud (*Private Collection*)

"Why must you be interrupting me, Madam, when I am thinking of something else?" And now and then, Miss Chauncey fancied he would deliberately secrete himself or steal out and in of Post Houses unbeknown.

Miss Chauncey, too, would sometimes find him trotting from room to room as if on a visit of inspection. On his fifth birthday he had brought an immense mouse and laid it beside the patent toe-cap of her boot, as she sat knitting by the fire. She smiled and nodded merrily at him, as usual, but on this occasion he had looked at her intently, and then deliberately shook his head. After that, he never paid the smallest attention to mouse or mouse-hole or mousery, and Miss Chauncey was obliged to purchase a cheese-bait trap, else she would have been overrun.

Almost any domestic cat may do things of this nature, and of course all this was solely on Sam's domestic side. For he shared a house with Miss Chauncey and, like any two beings that live together, he was bound to keep up certain appearances. He met her half-way, as the saying goes. When, however, he was "on his own", he was no longer Miss Chauncey's Sam, he was no longer merely the cat at Post Houses, but just *himself*. He went back, that is, to his own free independent life; to his own private habits.

Then the moor on which he roved was his own country, and the humans and their houses on it were no more to him in his wild, privy existence than molehills or badgers' earths, or rabbits' mounds, are to us. On this side of his life his mistress knew practically nothing. She did not consider it. She supposed that Sam behaved like other cats, though it was evident that at times he went far abroad, for he now and then brought home a Cochin China chick, and the nearest Cochin China fowls were at the vicarage, a good four miles off. Sometimes of an evening, too, when Miss Chauncey was taking a little walk herself, she would see him—a swiftly-moving black speck—far along the road, hastening home. And there was more purpose expressed in his gait and appearance than ever Mr Cullings showed!

It was pleasant to observe, too, when he came within miaouing distance how his manner changed. He turned at once from being a Cat into being a Domestic Cat. He was instantaneously no longer the Feline Adventurer, the Nocturnal Marauder and Haunter of Haggurdsdon Moor (though Miss Chauncey would not have so expressed it), but simply his mistress' spoiled pet, Sam. She loved him dearly. But, as again with human beings who are accustomed to live together, she did not *think* very much about him. It could not but be a shock then that latish afternoon, when without the slightest warning Miss Chauncey discovered that Sam was deliberately deceiving her!

She was brushing her thin brown front hair before her looking-glass. And this moment it hung down over her face like a fine loose veil. And as she always mused of other things when she was brushing her hair, she was somewhat absentminded the while. Then suddenly on raising her eyes behind this mesh of hair, she perceived not only that Sam's reflection was in sight of the looking-glass, but that something a little mysterious was happening. Sam was sitting up as if to beg. There was nothing in that. It had been a customary feat of his since he was six months old. Still, for what might he be begging, no one by?

Now the window to the right of the chintz-valanced dressing-table was open at the top. Without, it was beginning to grow dark. All Haggurdsdon Moor lay hushed and still in the evening's coming gloom. And apart from begging when there was nothing to beg for, Sam seemed, so to speak, to be gesticulating with his paws. He appeared, that is, to be making signs, just as if there were someone or something looking in at the window at him from out of the air—which was quite impossible. And there was a look upon his face that certainly Miss Chauncey had never seen before.

She stayed a moment with her hair-brush uplifted, her long lean arm at an angle with her

Paris Through the Window, Marc Chagall (*The Solomon R. Guggenheim Museum, New York*)

head. On seeing this, Sam had instantly desisted from these motions. He had dropped to his fours again, and was now apparently composing himself for another nap. No; this too was a pretence, for presently as she watched, he turned restlessly about so that his whiskers were once again due South. His backward part toward the window, he was now gazing straight in front of him out of a far from friendly face. Far indeed from friendly for a creature that has lived with you ever since he opened the eyes of his first kittenhood.

As if he had read her thoughts, Sam at that moment lifted his head to look at his mistress; she withdrew her eyes to the glass only in the nick of time and when she turned from her toilet there sat he—so serene in appearance, so puss-like, so ordinary once more that Miss Chauncey could scarcely believe anything whatever had been amiss. Had her eyes deluded her—her glass? Was that peculiar motion of Sam's fore-paws (almost as if he were knitting), was that wide excited stare only due to the fact that he was catching what was, to her, an invisible fly?

Miss Chauncey having now neatly arranged her "window-curtains"—the sleek loops of hair she wore on either side her high forehead—glanced yet again at the window. Nothing there but the silence of the moor; nothing there but the faint pricking of a star as the evening darkened.

Sam's cream was waiting on the hearthrug in the parlour as usual at five o'clock. The lamp was lit. The red blinds were drawn. The fire crackled in the grate. There they sat, these two; the walls of the four-cornered house beside the crossroads rising up above them like a huge oblong box under the immense starry sky that saucered in the wide darkness of the moor.

And while she so sat—with Sam there, seemingly fast asleep—Miss Chauncey was thinking. What had occurred in the bedroom that early evening had reminded her of other odd little bygone happenings. Trifles she had scarcely noticed but which now returned clearly to memory. How often in the past, for example, Sam at this hour would be sitting as if fast asleep (as now) his paws tucked neatly in, looking much like a stout alderman after a high dinner. And then suddenly, without warning, as if a distant voice had called him, he would leap to his feet and run straight out of the room. And somewhere in the house—door ajar or window agape, he would find his egress and be up and away into the night. This had been a common thing to happen.

Once, too, Miss Chauncey had found him squatting on his hind-quarters on the window-ledge of a little room that had been entirely disused since her fair little Cousin Milly had stayed at Post Houses when Miss Chauncey was a child of eight. She had cried out at sight of him, "You foolish Sam, you! Come in, sir. You will be tumbling out of the window next!" And she remembered as if it were yesterday that though at this he had stepped gingerly in at once from his dizzy perch, he had not looked at her. He had passed her without a sign.

On moonlight evenings, too—why, you could never be sure where he was. You could never be sure from what errand he had *returned*. Was she sure indeed where he was on *any* night? The longer she reflected, the deeper grew her doubts and misgivings. This night, at any rate, Miss Chauncey determined to keep watch. But she was not happy in doing so. She hated all manner of spying. They were old companions, Sam and she; and she, without him, in bleak Post Houses, would be sadly desolate. She loved Sam dearly. None the less, the spectacle of that afternoon haunted her, and it would be wiser to know all that there was to be known, even if for Sam's sake only.

Now Miss Chauncey always slept with her bedroom door ajar. She had slept so ever since her nursery days. Being a rather timid little girl, she liked in those far-away times to hear the grown-up voices downstairs and the spoons and forks clinking. As for Sam, he always slept in his basket beside her fireplace. Every morning there he would be, though on some mornings Miss Chauncey's eyes would open gently to find herself gazing steadily into his pale-green ones as he stood on his hind-paws, resting his front ones on her bed-side, and looking up into her face. "Time for your milk, Sam?" his mistress would murmur. And Sam would mew, as distantly almost as a seagull in the height of the sky.

Tonight, however, Miss Chauncey only pretended to fall asleep. It was difficult, however, to keep wholly awake, and she was all but drowsing off when there came a faint squeak from the hinge of her door, and she realised that Sam was gone out. After waiting a moment or two, she struck a match. Yes, there was his empty basket in the dark silent room, and presently from far away—from the steeple at Haggurdsdon Village—came the knolling of midnight.

Miss Chauncey placed the dead end of the match in the saucer of her candlestick, and at that moment fancied she heard a faint *whssh* at her window, as of a sudden gust or scurry of wind, or the wings of a fast-flying bird—of a wild goose. It even reminded Miss Chauncey of half-forgotten Guy Fawkes Days and of the sound the stick of a rocket makes as it sweeps down through the air while its green and ruby lights die out in the immense heavens above. Miss Chauncey gathered up her long legs in the bed, drew on the flannel dressing-gown that always hung on her bed-rail, and lifting back the blind an inch or two, looked out of the window.

It was a high starry night, and a brightening in the sky above the roof seemed to betoken

Animals in a Fantasy Landscape, Otto Dix (*Kunstmuseum Düsseldorf*)

there must be a moon over the backward parts of the house. Even as she watched, a streak of pale silver descended swiftly out of the far spaces of the heavens where a few large stars were gathered as if in the shape of a sickle. It was a meteorite; and at that very instant Miss Chauncey fancied she heard a faint remote dwindling *whssh* in the air. Was *that* a meteor too? Could she have been deceived? Was she being deceived in everything? She drew back.

And then, as if in deliberate and defiant answer, out of the distance, from what appeared to be the extreme end of her long garden, where grew a tangle of sloe bushes, there followed a prolonged and as if half-secret caterwaul; very low—contralto, one might say—*Meearou-rou-rou-rou-rou.*

Heaven forbid! Was *that* Sam's tongue? The caterwauling ceased. Yet still Miss Chauncey could not suppress a shudder. She knew Sam's voice of old. But surely not that! Surely not that!

Strange and immodest, too, though it was to hear herself in that solitary place calling out in the dead of night, she none the less at once opened the window and summoned Sam by name. There was no response. The trees and bushes of the garden stood motionless; their faint shadows on the ground revealing how small a moon was actually in the sky, and how low it hung towards its setting. The vague undulations of the moor stretched into the distance. Not a light to be seen except those of the firmament. Again, and yet again, Miss Chauncey cried, "Sam, Sam! Come away in! Come away in, sir, you bad creature!" Not a sound. Not the least stir of leaf or blade of grass.

When, after so broken a night, Miss Chauncey awoke a little late the next morning, the first thing her eyes beheld when she sat up in bed was Sam—couched as usual in his basket. It was a mystery, an uneasy one. After supping up his morning bowl, he slept steadily on until noonday. This happened to be the day of the week when Miss Chauncey made bread. On and on she steadily kneaded the dough with her knuckled hands, glancing ever and again towards the motionless creature. With fingers clotted from the great earthenware bowl, she stood over him at last for a few moments, and looked at him closely.

He was lying curled round with his whiskered face to one side towards the fire. And it seemed to Miss Chauncey that she had never noticed before that faint peculiar grin on his face. "Sam!" she cried sharply. An eye instantly opened, fiercely green as if a mouse had squeaked. He stared at her for an instant; then the lid narrowed. The gaze slunk away a little, but Sam began to purr.

The truth of it is, all this was making Miss Chauncey exceedingly unhappy. Mr Cullings called that afternoon with a basket of some fine comely young sprats. "Them'll wake his Royal Highness up," he said. "They'm fresh as daisies. Lor, m'm, what a Nero that beast be!"

"Cats *are* strange creatures, Mr Cullings," replied Miss Chauncey reflectively, complacently, supposing that Mr Cullings had misplaced an *h* and had meant to say *an hero*. And Sam himself, with uplifted tail, and as if of the same opinion, was rubbing his head gently against her boot.

Mr Cullings eyed her closely. "Why, yes, they be," he said. "What I says is, is that as soon as they're out of sight, you are out of their mind. There's no more gratitood nor affection in a cat than in a pump. Though so far as the pump is concerned, the gratitood should be on our side. I knew a Family of Cats once what fairly druv their mistress out of house and home."

"But you wouldn't have a cat *only* a pet?" said Miss Chauncey faintly; afraid to ask for further particulars of the peculiar occurrence.

"Why no, m'm," said the carrier. "As the Lord made 'em, so they be. But I'll be bound they could tell some knotty stories if they had a human tongue in their heads!"

Sam had ceased caressing his mistress's foot, and was looking steadily at Mr Cullings, his hair roughed a little about the neck and shoulders. And the carrier looked back.

"No, m'm. We wouldn't keep 'em," he said at last, "if they was *four* times that size. Or, not for long!"

Having watched Mr Cullings' little cart bowl away into the distance, Miss Chauncey returned into the house, more disturbed than ever. Nor did her uneasiness abate when Sam refused even to sniff at his sprats. Instead, he crawled under a low table in the kitchen, behind the old seaman's chest in which Miss Chauncey kept her kindling-wood. She fancied she heard his claws working in the wood now and again; once he seemed to be expressing his natural feelings in what vulgar people with little sympathy for animals describe as "swearing".

Her caressing "Sams", at any rate, were all in vain. His only reply was a kind of sneeze which uncomfortably resembled "spitting". Miss Chauncey's feelings had already been hurt. It was now her mind that suffered. Something the carrier had said, or the way he had said it, or the peculiar look she had noticed on his face when he was returning Sam's stare in the porch, haunted her thoughts. She was no longer young; was she becoming fanciful? Or must she indeed conclude that for weeks past Sam had been steadily deceiving her, or at any rate concealing his wanderings and his interests? What nonsense! Worse still:—Was she now so credulous as to believe that Sam had in actual fact been making signals—and secretly, behind her back—to some confederate that must either have been up in the sky, or in the moon!

Witches from *The Book of Days*

Whether or not, Miss Chauncey determined to keep a sharper eye on him, if for his own sake only. She would at least make sure that he did not leave the house that night. But then: why not? she asked herself. Why shouldn't the creature choose his own hour and season? Cats, like owls, *see* best in the dark. They go best a-mousing in the dark, and may prefer the dark for their private, social, and even public affairs. Post Houses, after all, was only rather more than two miles from Haggurdsdon Village, and there were cats there in plenty. Poor fellow, her own dumb human company must sometimes be dull enough!

Such were Miss Chauncey's reflections; and as if to reassure her, Sam himself at that moment serenely entered the room and leaped up on to the empty chair beside her tea-table. As if, too, to prove that he had thought better of his evil temper, or to insinuate that there had been nothing amiss between himself and Mr Cullings, he was licking his chops, and there was no mistaking the odour of fish which he brought in with him from his saucer.

"So you have thought better of it, my boy?" thought Miss Chauncey, though she did not utter the words aloud. And yet as she returned his steady feline gaze, she realised how difficult it was to read the intelligence behind those eyes. You might say that, Sam being only a cat, there was no meaning in them at all. But Miss Chauncey knew she couldn't have said it if such eyes

[124]

had looked out of a *human* shape at her! She would have been acutely alarmed.

Unfortunately, and almost as if Sam had overheard his mistress' speculations regarding possible cat friends in the Village, there came at that moment a faint wambling mew beneath the open window. In a flash Sam was out of his chair and over the window ledge, and Miss Chauncey rose only just in time to see him in infuriated pursuit of a slim sleek tortoiseshell creature that had evidently come to Post Houses in hope of a friendlier reception, and was now fleeing in positive fear of its life.

Sam returned from his chase as fresh as paint, and Miss Chauncey was horrified to detect—caught up between the claws of his right foot—a tuft or two or tortoiseshell fur, which, having composed himself by the fire, he promptly removed by licking.

Still pondering on these disquieting events, Miss Chauncey took her usual evening walk in the garden. Candytuft and Virginia stock were blossoming along the shell-lined path, and roses were already beginning to blow on the high brick wall which shut off her narrow strip of land from the vast lap of the moor. Having come to the end of the path, Miss Chauncey pushed on a little farther than usual, to where the grasses grew more rampant, and where wild headlong weeds raised their heads beneath her few lichenous apple trees. Still farther down—for hers was a long, though narrow, garden—there grew straggling bushes of sloe, spiny white-thorn. These had blossomed there indeed in the moor's bleak springs long before Post Houses had raised its chimney-pots into the sky. Here, too, flourished a dense drift of dead-nettles—their sour odour haunting the air.

And it was in this forlorn spot that—like Robinson Crusoe before her—Miss Chauncey was suddenly brought to a standstill by the sight of what appeared to be nothing else than a strange footprint in the mould. Nearby the footprint, moreover, showed what might be the impression of a walking-cane or possibly of something stouter and heavier—a crutch. Could she again be deceived? The footprint, it was true, was unlike most human footprints, the heel sunk low, the toe square. Might it be accidental? *Was* it a footprint?

Miss Chauncey glanced up across the bushes toward the house. It loomed gaunt and forbidding in the moorland dusk. And she fancied she could see, though the evening light might be deceiving her, the cowering shape of Sam looking out at her from the kitchen-window. To be watched! To be herself spied upon—and watched.

But then of course, Sam was always watching her. What oddity was there in that? Where else would his sprats come from, his cream, his saucer of milk, his bowl of fresh well-water? Nevertheless Miss Chauncey returned to her parlour gravely discomposed.

It was an uncommonly still evening, and as she went from room to room locking the windows, she noticed there was already a moon in the sky. She eyed it with misgiving. And at last bedtime came, and when Sam, as usual after a lick or two had composed himself in his basket, Miss Chauncey, holding the key almost challengingly within view, deliberately locked her bedroom door.

When she awoke next morning Sam was sleeping in his basket as usual, and during the daytime he kept pretty closely to the house. So, too, on the Wednesday and the Thursday. It was not until the following Friday that having occasion to go into an upper bedroom that had no fireplace, and being followed as usual by Sam, Miss Chauncey detected the faint rank smell of soot in the room. No chimney, and a smell of soot! She turned rapidly on her companion; he had already left the room.

And when that afternoon she discovered a black sooty smear upon her own patchwork quilt, she realised not only that her suspicions had been justified, but that for the first time in his life Sam had deliberately laid himself down there in her absence. At this act of sheer defiance, she was no longer so much hurt as exceedingly angry. There was no doubt now. Sam was deliberately defying her. No two companions could share a house on such terms as these. He must be taught a lesson.

That evening in full sight of the creature, having locked her bedroom door, she stuffed a large piece of mattress ticking into the mouth of her chimney and pulled down the register. Having watched these proceedings, Sam rose from his basket, and with an easy spring, leapt up on to the dressing-table. Beyond the window, the moor lay almost as bright as day. Ignoring Miss Chauncey, the creature squatted there steadily and openly staring into the empty skies, for a whole stretch of them was visible from where he sat.

Miss Chauncey proceeded to make her toilet for the night, trying in vain to pretend that she was entirely uninterested in what the animal was at. Faint sounds—not exactly mewings or growlings—but a kind of low inward caterwauling, hardly audible, was proceeding from his throat. But whatever these sounds might mean, Sam himself can have been the only listener. There was not a sign or movement at the window or in the world without. And then Miss Chauncey promptly drew down the blind. At this Sam at once raised his paw for all the world as if he were about to protest, and then, apparently thinking better of it, he pretended instead that the action had been only for the purpose of commencing his nightly wash.

Long after her candle had been extinguished, Miss Chauncey lay listening. Every stir and movement in the quiet darkness could be clearly followed. First there came a furtive footing and tapping at the register of the fireplace, so closely showing what was happening that Miss Chaun-

Villagers Attacking a Witch

[126]

cey could positively see in her imagination Sam on the hearth-stone, erecting himself there upon his hind-legs, vainly attempting to push the obstacle back.

This being in vain, he appeared to have dropped back on to his fours. Then came a pause. Had he given up his intention? No; now he was at the door, pawing, gently scratching. Then a leap, even towards the handle; but one only—the door was locked. Retiring from the door, he now sprang lightly again on to the dressing-table. What now was he at? By covertly raising her head from her pillow, Miss Chauncey could see him with paw thrust out, gently drawing back the blind from the moon-flooded window-pane. And even while she listened and watched, she heard yet again—and yet again—the faint *whssh* as of a wild swan cleaving the air; and then what might have been the cry of a bird, but which to Miss Chauncey's ears resembled a shrill cackle of laughter. At this Sam hastily turned from the window and without the least attempt at concealment pounced clean from the dressing-table on to the lower rail of her bed.

This unmannerly conduct could be ignored no longer. Poor Miss Chauncey raised herself in her sheets, pulled her night-cap a little closer down over her ears, and thrusting out her hand towards the chair beside the bed, struck a match and relit her candle. It was with a real effort that she then slowly turned her head and faced her night-companion. His hair was bristling about his body as if he had had an electric shock. His whiskers stood out at stiff angles with his jaws. He looked at least twice his usual size, and his eyes blazed in his head, as averting his face from her regard he gave vent to a low sustained *Miariou-rou-rou!*

"I say you shall *not*," cried Miss Chauncey at the creature. At the sound of her words, he turned slowly and confronted her. And it seemed that until that moment Miss Chauncey had never actually seen Sam's countenance as in actual fact it really was. It was not so much the grinning tigerish look it wore, but the sullen assurance upon it of what he wanted and that he meant to get it.

All thought of sleep was out of the question. Miss Chauncey could be obstinate too. The creature seemed to shed an influence on the very air which she could hardly resist. She rose from her bed and thrusting on her slippers made her way to the window. Once more a peculiar inward cry broke out from the bed-rail. She raised the blind and the light of the moon from over the moor swept in upon her little apartment. And when she turned to remonstrate with her pet at his ingratitude, and at all this unseemliness and the deceit of his ways, there was something so menacing and pitiless in his aspect that Miss Chauncey hesitated no more.

"Well, mark me!" she cried in a trembling voice. "Go out of the *door* you shan't. But if you enjoy soot, soot it shall be."

With that she thrust back the register with the poker, and drew down the bundle of ticking with the tongs. And before the fit of coughing caused by the consequent smotheration that followed had ceased, the lithe black shape had sprung from the bed-rail, and with a scramble was into the hearth, over the firebars, up the chimney, and away.

Trembling from head to foot, Miss Chauncey sat down on a cane rocking-chair that stood nearby to reflect what next she must be doing. *Wh-ssh! Wh-ssh!* Again at the window came that mysterious rushing sound, but now the flurrying murmur as of a rocket shooting up with its fiery train of sparks thinning into space, rather than the sound of its descending stick. And then in the hush that followed, there sounded yet again, like a voice from the foot of the garden—a caterwauling piercing and sonorous enough to arouse the sleeping cocks in the Haggurdsdon hen-roosts and for miles around. Out of the distance their chanticleering broke shrill on the night air; to be followed a moment afterwards by the tardy clang of midnight from the church steeple. Then once more silence; utter quiet. Miss Chauncey returned to her bed, but that night she slept no more.

Her mind overflowed with unhappy thoughts. Her faith in Sam was gone. Far worse she had lost faith even in her affection for him. To have wasted that!—all the sprats, all the white-bait in the wide seas were as nothing by comparison. That Sam had wearied of her company was at least beyond question. It shamed her to think how much this meant to her—a mere animal! But she knew what was gone; knew how dull and spiritless in future the day's round would seem —the rising, the housework, the meals, a clean linen collar—the long, slow afternoon, forsaken and companionless! The solitary tea, her candle, prayers, bed—on and on. It what wild company was her cat Sam now? At her own refusal to face that horrid question it was as if she had heard the hollow clanging slam of an immense iron door.

Next morning—still ruminating on these strange events, grieved to the heart at this dreadful rift between herself and one who had been her honest companion of so many years; ashamed, too, that Sam should have had his way with her when she had determined not to allow him to go out during the night—the next morning Miss Chauncey, as if merely to take a little exercise, once again ventured down to the foot of her garden. A faint, blurred mark (such as she had seen on the previous evening) in the black mould of what *might* be a footprint is nothing very much.

But now—in the neglected patch beyond the bushes of white-thorn and bramble—there was no doubt in the world appeared the marks of many. And surely no cats' paw-prints these! Of what use, too, to a cat could a crutch or a staff be? A staff or crutch which—to judge from the impression it had left in the mould—must have been at least as thick as a broomstick.

More disquieted and alarmed than ever over this fresh mystery, Miss Chauncey glanced up

Witches, Francisco de Goya (*Museo del Prado, Madrid*)

[128]

and back towards the chimney-pots of the house, clearly and sharply fretted against the morning light of the eastern skies. And she realised what perils even so sure-footed a creature as Sam had faced when he skirred up out of the chimney in his wild effort to emerge into the night. Having thus astonishingly reached the rim of the chimney-pot—the burning stars above and the wilderness of the moor spread out far beneath and around him—he must have leaped from the top of the pot to a narrow brick ledge not three inches wide. Thence on to the peak of the roof and thence down a steep slippery slope of slates to a leaden gutter.

And how then? The thick tod of ivy matting the walls of the house reached hardly more than half-way up. Could Sam actually have plunged from gutter to tod? The very thought of such peril drew Miss Chauncey's steps towards the house again, in the sharpest anxiety to assure herself that he was still in the land of the living.

And lo and behold, when she was but half-way on her journey, she heard a succession of frenzied cries and catcalls in the air from over the moor. Hastily placing a flower-pot by the wall, she stood on tiptoe and peered over. And even now, at this very moment, in full sight across the nearer slope of the moor she descried her Sam, not now in chase of a foolishly trustful visitor, but hotly pursued by what appeared to be the complete rabblement of Haggurdsdon's cats. Sore spent though he showed himself to be, Sam was keeping his distance. Only a few lank tabby gibs, and what appeared to be a gray-ginger Manx (unless he was an ordinary cat with his tail chopped off) were close behind.

"Sam! Sam!" Miss Chauncey cried, and yet again, "Sam!" but in her excitement and anxiety her foot slipped on the flower-pot and in an instant the feline chase had fallen out of sight. Gathering herself together again, she clutched a long besom or garden broom that was leaning against the wall, and rushed down to the point at which she judged Sam would make his entrance into the garden. She was not mistaken, nor an instant too soon. With a bound he was up and over, and in three seconds the rabble had followed in frenzied pursuit.

What came after Miss Chauncey could never very clearly recall. She could but remember plying her besom with might and main amid the rabble and mêlée of animals, while Sam, no longer a fugitive, turned on his enemies and fought them cat for cat. None the less, it was by no means an easy victory. And had not the over-fatted cur from the butcher's in Haggurdsdon— which had long since started in pursuit of this congregation of his enemies—had he not at last managed to overtake them, the contest might very well have had a tragic ending. But at the sound of his baying and at sight of the cur's teeth snapping at them as he vainly attempted to surmount the wall, Sam's enemies turned and fled in all directions. And faint and panting, Miss Chauncey was able to fling down her besom and to lean for a brief respite against the trunk of a tree.

At last she opened her eyes again. "Well, Sam," she managed to mutter at last, "we got the best of them, then?"

But to her amazement she found herself uttering these friendly words into a complete vacancy. The creature was nowhere to be seen. His cream disappeared during the day, however, and by an occasional rasping sound Miss Chauncey knew that he once more lay hidden in his dingy resort behind the kindling-wood box. And there she did not disturb him.

Not until tea-time of the following day did Sam reappear. And then—after attending to his hurts—it was merely to sit with face towards the fire, sluggish and sullen and dumb as a dog. It was not Miss Chauncey's "place" to make advances, she thought. She took no notice of the beast except to rub in a little hog's fat on the raw places of his wounds. She was rejoiced to find, however, that he kept steadily to Post Houses for the next few days, though her dismay was reawakened at hearing on the third night a more dismal wailing and wauling than ever from the sloe-bushes, even while Sam himself sat motionless beside the fire. His ears twitched, his fur seemed by bristle; he sneezed or spat, but remained otherwise motionless.

When Mr Cullings called again, Sam at once hid himself in the coal-cellar, but gradually his manners toward Miss Chauncey began to recover their usual suavity. And within a fortnight after the full-moon, the two of them had almost returned to their old friendly companionship. He was healed, sleek, confident and punctual. No intruder of his species had appeared from Haggurdsdon. The night noises had ceased; Post Houses to all appearances—apart from its strange ugliness—was as peaceful and calm as any other solitary domicile in the United Kingdom.

But alas and alas. With the very first peeping of the crescent moon, Sam's mood and habits began to change again. He mouched about with a sly and furtive eye. And when he fawned on her, purring and clawing, the whole look of him was full of deceit. If Miss Chauncey chanced softly to enter the room wherein he sat, he would at once leap down from the window at which he had been perched as if in the attempt to prove that he had *not* been looking out of it. And once, towards evening, though she was no spy, she could not but pause at the parlour door. She had peeped through its crack as it stood ajar. And there on the hard sharp back of an old prie-dieu

Sacred Cat (British Museum)

[130]

chair that had belonged to her pious great-aunt Jemima, there sat Sam on his hind-quarters. And without the least doubt in the world he was vigorously signalling to some observer outside with his forepaws. Miss Chauncey turned away sick at heart.

From that hour on Sam more and more steadily ignored and flouted his mistress, was openly insolent, shockingly audacious. Mr Cullings gave her small help indeed. "If I had a cat, m'm, what had manners like that, after all your kindness, fresh fish and all every week, and cream, as I understand, not skim, I'd—I'd give him away."

"To whom?" said Miss Chauncey shortly.

"Well," said the carrier, "I don't know as how I'd much mind to who. Just a home, m'm."

"He seems to have no friends in the Village," said Miss Chauncey in as light a tone as she could manage.

"When they're as black as that, with them saucer eyes, you can never tell," said Mr Cullings. "There's that old trollimog what lives in Hogges Bottom. She's got a cat that might be your Sam's twin."

"Indeed no, he has the mange," said Miss Chauncey, loyal to the end. The carrier shrugged his shoulders, climbed into his cart, and bowled away off over the moor. And Miss Chauncey returning into the house, laid the platter of silvery sprats on the table, sat down and burst into tears.

It was, then, in most ways a fortunate thing that the very next morning—three complete days, that is, before the next full-moontide—she received a letter from her sister-in-law in Shanklin, in the Isle of Wight, entreating her to pay them a long visit.

"My dear Emma, you must sometimes be feeling very lonely (it ran), shut up in that great house so far from any neighbours. We often think of you, and particularly these last few days. It's nice to have that Sam of yours for company, but after all, as George says, a pet is only a pet. And we do all think it's high time you took a little holiday with us. I am looking out of my window at this moment. The sea is as calm as a mill-pond, a solemn beautiful blue. The fishing boats are coming in with their brown sails. This is the best time of the year with us, because as it's not yet holy-day-time there are few of those horrid visitors to be seen, and no crowds. George says you *must* come. He joins with me in his love as would Maria if she weren't out shopping, and will meet you at the station in the trap. Emmie is now free of her cough, only whooping when the memory takes her and never sick. And we shall all be looking forward to seeing you in a few days."

At this kindness, and with all her anxieties, Miss Chauncey all but broke down. When the butcher drove up in his cart an hour or two afterwards, he took a telegram for her back to the Village, and on the Monday her box was packed and all that remained was to put Sam in his basket in preparation for the journey. But I am bound to say it took more than the persuasion of his old protectress to accomplish this. Indeed Mr Cullings had actually to hold the creature with his gloved hands and none too gently, while Miss Chauncey pressed down the lid and pushed the skewer in to hold it close.

"What's done's dumned done!" said the carrier, as he rubbed a pinch of earth into his scratches. "But what I say is, better done forever. Mark my words, m'm!"

Miss Chauncey took a shilling out of her large leather purse; but made no reply.

Indeed all this trouble proved at last in vain. Thirty miles distant from Haggurdsdon, at Blackmoor Junction, Miss Chauncey had to change trains. Her box and Sam's basket were placed together on the station platform beside half-a-dozen empty milk-cans and some fowls in a crate, and Miss Chauncey went to enquire of the station-master to make sure of her platform.

It was the furious panic-stricken cackling of these fowls that brought her hastily back to her belongings, only to find that by hook or by crook Sam had managed to push the skewer of the basket out of its cane loops. The wicker lid yawned open—the basket was empty. Indeed one poor gaping hen, its life fluttering away from its helpless body, was proof not only of Sam's prowess but of his cowardly ferocity.

A few days afterwards, as Miss Chauncey sat in the very room to which her sister-in-law had referred in her invitation, looking over the placid surface of the English Channel, the sun gently shining in the sky, there came a letter from Mr Cullings. It was in pencil and written upon the back of a baker's bag:

"Dear Madam, i take the libberty of riteing you in referense to the Animall as how i helped put in is bawskit which has cum back returned empty agenn by rail me having okashun to cart sum hop powles from Haggurdsdon late at nite ov Sunday. I seez him squattin at the parlor windy grimasin out at me fit to curdle your blood in your vanes and lights at the upper windies and a yowling and screetching such as i never hopes to hear agen in a Christian lokalety. And that ole wumman from Hogges Botom sitting in the porch mi own vew being that there is no good in the place and the Animall be bewitched. Mr Flint the fyshmunger agrees with me as how now only last mesures is of any use and as i have said afore i am wiling to take over the house the rent if so be being low and moddrate considering of the bad name it as in these parts around Haggurdsdon. I remain dear madam waitin your orders and oblidge yours truely William Cullings."

To look at Miss Chauncey you might have supposed she was a strong-minded woman. You might have supposed that this uncivil reference to the bad name her family house had won for itself would have mortified her beyond words. Whether or not, she neither showed this letter to her sister-in-law nor for many days together did she even answer it. Sitting on the Esplanade, and looking out to sea, she brooded on and on in the warm, salt, yet balmy air. It was a distressing problem. But, "No, he must go his own way," she sighed to herself at last; "I have done my best for him."

What is more, Miss Chauncey never returned to Post Houses. She sold it at last, house and garden and for a pitiful sum, to the carrier, Mr Cullings. By that time Sam had vanished, had been never seen again.

Not that Miss Chauncey was faithless of memory. Whenever the faint swish of a seagull's wing sounded in the air above her head; or the crackling of an ascending rocket for the amusement of the visitors broke the silence of the nearer heavens over the sea; whenever even she became conscious of the rustling frou-frou of her Sunday watered-silk gown as she sallied out to church from the neat little villa she now rented on the Shanklin Esplanade—she never noticed such things without being instantly transported back in imagination to her bedroom at Post Houses, to see again that strange deluded animal, once her Sam, squatting there on her patchwork counterpane, and as it were knitting with his fore-paws the while he stood erect upon his hind.

The Cat and the Moon

W. B. Yeats

The cat went here and there
And the moon spun round like a top,
And the nearest kin of the moon,
The creeping cat, looked up.
Black Minnaloushe stared at the moon,
For, wander and wail as he would,
The pure cold light in the sky
Troubled his animal blood.
Minnaloushe runs in the grass
Lifting his delicate feet.
Do you dance, Minnaloushe, do you dance?

The Mount of the Sacred Cat, Paul Klee (*Private Collection*)

When two close kindred meet,
What better than call a dance?
Maybe the moon may learn,
Tired of that courtly fashion,
A new dance turn.
Minnaloushe creeps through the grass
From moonlit place to place,
The sacred moon overhead
Has taken a new phase.
Does Minnaloushe know that his pupils
Will pass from change to change,
And that from round to crescent,
From crescent to round they range?
Minnaloushe creeps through the grass
Alone, important and wise,
And lifts to the changing moon
His changing eyes.

Diamond Cut Diamond

Ewart Milne

Two cats
One up a tree
One under the tree
The cat up a tree is he
The cat under the tree is she
The tree is witch elm, just incidentally.
He takes no notice of she, she takes no notice of he.
He stares at the woolly clouds passing, she stares at the tree.
There's been a lot written about cats, by Old Possum, Yeats and Company
But not Alfred de Musset or Lord Tennyson or Poe or anybody
Wrote about one cat under, and one cat up, a tree.
God knows why this should be left for me
Except I like cats as cats be
Especially one cat up
And one under
A witch elm
Tree

Two Cats (Mansell Collection)

The Cat

Giles Lytton Strachey

Dear creature by the fire a-purr,
    Strange idol, eminently bland,
Miraculous puss! As o'er your fur
    I trail a negligible hand

And gaze into your gazing eyes,
    And wonder in a demi-dream
What mystery it is that lies
    Behind those slits that glare and gleam,

An exquisite enchantment falls
    About the portals of my sense;
Meandering through enormous halls
    I breathe luxurious frankincense.

An ampler air, a warmer June
    Enfold me, and my wondering eye
Salutes a more imperial moon
    Throned in a more resplendent sky

Than ever knew this northern shore.
    Oh, strange! For you are with me too,
And I, who am a cat once more,
    Follow the woman that was you.

With tail erect and pompous march,
    The proudest puss that ever trod,
Through many a grove, 'neath many an arch,
    Impenetrable as a god,

Down many an alabaster flight
    Of broad and cedar-shaded stairs,
While over us the elaborate night
    Mysteriously gleams and glares!

Cat on the Floor, Théophile Steinlen (*Achenbach Foundation, California Palace of the Legion of Honor, San Francisco*)

The Cat Horoscope

Ann Currah

ARIES (March 21–April 20): The original cat on a hot tin roof, most active and ambitious of them all. From clean laundry to flower beds, he makes a (hollow) impression everywhere. Fond of wandering, and when at home liable to create his own obstacle course with no inhibitions about broken ornaments. Fond of fighting, impetuous at loving.
Best Owners (only owners able to survive him): Sagittarius, Leo.

TAURUS (April 21–May 20): So placid and imperturbable that humans can understand him. So far from flighty that even danger will not stir his lazy bones. Taurus is dependable—you can depend on him to be forever in your way.
Best Owners: Capricorn, Virgo, Cancer.

GEMINI (May 21–June 20): Essentially the kitten-cat, that exaggeratedly playful pussy with the gift of eternal youth. So far as felines fret, Gemini frets. He desires change of scene, balls of wool; is much in demand for TV commercials. Incorrigibly bossy.
Best Owners: Libra, Aquarius, but never Taurus.

CANCER (June 21–July 20): Inconstant as the moon, deceitful as women, emotional as a Foreign Secretary, he swings from the chandelier and meows piteously in the corner; nobody can understand this cat. Regards humans as furniture.
Best Owners: Pisces, Scorpio.

LEO (July 21–August 21): Pretentious—like his sign—authoritative, domineering, and ostentatious. From kittenhood, goes through life with the look of one who has his nose immediately above the smell of a rotting mouse. No tabby can resist him.
Best Owners: Aries, Sagittarius, but never Capricorn.

VIRGO (August 22–September 22): Conscientious, dedicated, down-to-earth. So domesticated that if you leave the beds until teatime, he glowers in disapproval. Careful never to harm a growing petunia, fussy enough to demand fresh food. Choosy about friends.
Best Owners: Capricorn, Taurus.

LIBRA (September 23–October 22): Remember copy cats? That's Libra—which is why he studies his owner to an extent, learning his mannerisms, adopting his habits. He prefers to look at life from your lap, to breakfast off eggs and bacon.
Best Owners: Leo, but never Aries.

SCORPIO (October 23–November 22): Hidden beneath his prettily patterned fur lurks enough power for a fleet of bulldozers. Nobody ever got the better of this cat. He sums you up from the start. A hospitable cat, usually at your expense; likely to expect you to maintain his mate.
Best Owners: Cancer, Pisces.

SAGITTARIUS (November 23–December 20): A dreamy cat with the speed of a horse but the brain of a bird. This unsettling combination usually makes him as uncomfortable as he makes you. Not good in town—a dilapidated castle or old manor keeps him happiest.
Best Owners: Sagittarius, Leo, but never Cancer.

CAPRICORN (December 21–January 19): A serious·cat, most aptly named Prudence; cool, deliberate, a calculating cat indeed. If he cannot improve his owners, then he seeks a new family. Quickly house-trained, but too flirty for a happy love life.
Best Owners: Virgo, Libra, Taurus.

AQUARIUS (January 20–February 18): Meddlesome moggie, keen to have a paw in everybody's business. Appears to be kleptomaniac, but only steals a neighbour's petticoat or next-door's strawberry plants because he heard you admire them. Fond of humans.
Best Owners: Libra, Gemini, Aquarius.

PISCES (February 19–March 20): A difficult cat, often gay and moody, friendly but uncommunicative at the same time. Easily placated with promises of "fish tomorrow". The ideal ship's cat or theatre cat, for he loves the sea as much as play-acting.
Best Owners: Cancer, Scorpio, but never Capricorn.

FROM
The Hsien-i

Liu Yuan-ch'ing
(translated by Martin Booth)

The Chi-Yen family kept a cat which the master of the house held very highly indeed, calling it *Tiger*. One day, a passer-by said to him, "A tiger is a ferocious creature, but not as strange and mystical as a dragon. Cats are so. I suggest you change the cat's name to *Dragon*."

Chinese Cats from *Jeux des nuages et de la pluie*

[139]

Not long afterwards, a stranger saw the cat and said, "A dragon is definitely more mysterious than a tiger. When it flies high in the firmament, it rests on the clouds. This means the clouds are greater than the dragon. So call the cat *Cloud*."

Others came by with their own ideas, furthering the idea and the development of the cat's name.

"When the clouds are heavy and grey, the wind dispels them: now that's great! The wind is the greatest thing in the world. Re-name your cat *Wind*."

"The wind is powerful: when a typhoon rises and screams about we shelter from it behind the walls of the house. They withstand the blast of the wind. The wall is the thing that holds back all power from us. The cat should be called *Wall*."

"So walls are strong. But when they are riddled with rat-holes, they are weakened, the wood splinters and the wall falls. Now cats hit out at rats: always have—they kill them. *Rat* would be a fitting name for your cat!"

Through all this, an old man from Tung-lii butted in. He laughed wryly and said, "No! No! Look, my friends, a cat's a cat. It lives to kill rats. Why try to change its way of being?"

Chinese Cat Merchants at the Port of Peking, T. Allom

FROM
A Voyage to Lisbon

Henry Fielding

Thursday, July 11th 1754. A most tragical incident fell out this day at sea. While the ship was under sail, but making as will appear no great way, a kitten, one of four of the feline inhabitants of the cabin, fell from the window into the water: an alarm was immediately given to the captain, who was then upon deck, and received it with the utmost concern and many bitter oaths. He immediately gave orders to the steersman in favour of the poor thing, as he called it; the sails were instantly slackened, and all hands, as the phrase is, employed to recover the poor animal. I was, I own, extremely surprised at all this; less indeed at the captain's extreme tenderness than at his conceiving any possibility of success; for if puss had had nine thousand instead of nine lives, I concluded they had been all lost. The boatswain, however, had more sanguine hopes, for having stripped himself of his jacket, breeches and shirt, he leaped boldly into the water, and to my great astonishment, in a few minutes returned to the ship, bearing the motionless animal in his mouth. Nor was this, I observed, a matter of such great difficulty as it appeared to my ignorance, and possibly may seem to that of my fresh-water reader. The kitten was now exposed to air and sun on the deck, where its life, of which it retained no symptoms, was despaired of by all.

The captain's humanity, if I may so call it, did not so totally destroy his philosophy as to make him yield himself up to affliction on this melancholy occasion. Having felt his loss like a man, he resolved to shew he could bear it like one; and, having declared he had rather have lost a cask of rum or brandy, betook himself to threshing at backgammon with the Portuguese friar, in which innocent amusement they passed about two-thirds of their time.

But as I have, perhaps, a little too wantonly endeavoured to raise the tender passions of my readers in this narrative, I should think myself unpardonable if I concluded it without giving them the satisfaction of hearing that the kitten at last recovered, to the great joy of the good captain, but to the great disappointment of some of the sailors, who asserted that the drowning cat was the very surest way of raising a favourable wind; a supposition of which, though we have heard several plausible accounts, we will not presume to assign the true original reason.

Wednesday. He even extended his humanity, if I may so call it, to animals, and even his cats and kittens had large shares in his affection. An instance of which we saw this evening, when the cat, which had shewn it could not be drowned, was found suffocated under a feather-bed in the cabin. I will not endeavour to describe his lamentations with more prolixity than barely by saying they were grievous, and seemed to have some mixture of the Irish howl in them.

Cats

Charles Baudelaire

(translated by Roy Fuller)

Lovers and austere dons are equally
(In their maturity) attached to cats—
Cats soft but cruel, emperors of flats,
Touchy like these and like those sedentary.

Friends of the sensual, the cerebral,
They seek the quiet and horror of the dark;
If they had ever bent their pride to work
They might have pulled the funeral cars of hell.

Asleep they take the noble attitude
Of the great sphinxes that appear to brood,
Stretched in the wastes, in dreams that have no end;
Their loins are electric with fecundity,
And particles of gold, like finest sand,
Star vaguely their unfathomable eye.

The Seventh Knight and the Green Cat: A Variation on the Gawain Poet

Alan Brownjohn

Curious about her seven daughters, in turn came
The seven fortitudinous knights. And the first
To sit by the swarming fire, sipping mead with

The Return of Odysseus, Pintoricchio (*National Gallery, London*)

Mother and eldest daughter, saw with much delight
The white cat pace to him, as he loved them,
Cats.
    The creature was unbleached to a queer
Shifting shade of green by the colours of the room
—Green hangings, green velvet on the couches,
Green branches at the window, green eyes in matron and girl,
Green even in the flames of the fire because
They cast salt in the crevices of the coals to
Make matching colours.
               So the white cat
Mewed at him, nudged his ankle, mounted his lap,
And the mother murmured, "You are much honoured.
She has never before walked in such a way up to a man."

This flattery went deep, the proposals were made, and the pair
Duly wed.
        And since daughters must dutifully marry,
And mothers must needs be mothers, and marry off,
A second knight came seeking the second daughter
And chose a green chair by the great fire while
The mother poured wine.
        Again, willingly, the white
Cat rose on her green cushion, stood stretching,
And pattered the flagstones to the handsome second knight
To form fond figures-of-eight round the man's thin legs.
"There's a something about you that attracts her, she
Has never lingered with any man," the lady said.
In this style was her second daughter secured
To a cat-adoring knight.
        This way it went too
With the third, the fourth, the fifth, and the sixth, on
A succession of green days with the cat casually
Trusting its truly said-to-be-so-untypical
Affection to the different knights, whether of
Aragon, Transylvania, Tartary or Tibet, being
Similar only in their peculiar pride at pre-empting,
Uniquely, an unsociable animal unsure of men:
Cat-lovers but gullible with it, which is rare.

On the last and greenest day, green curtains gathered
Across the storm which sent the green branches seething
Over the sky in a frenzied trellis-work of green,
The seventh knight finally knocked; one who knew
And loved cats more than any of these lovers, and
He yearned for the youngest daughter's hand.
        Her mother
Decanted liquor as usual, and the lovely daughter sat,
And green flames flashed in the hearth as the cat
Began again, greenly, its meaningful trek of the floor.
"She will not go to you, she has never gone to greet a man,"
The matron predicted; but the cat pounced all at once,
From no definable angle, on the very codpiece of the doting
Knight, and neatly nestled.
        So the mother and girl
Cried equally with eagerness and ecstasy as before

—At which the knight bounded up from his bench of green,
Shouting, "I am getting out, out of here at once!"
And "I know what sort of situation this is,"
Dropping the cat, flat-eared and snarling, with dire dismay,
To the stones, decapitating the thing with a dirk;

[144]

European with Servants, c.1605–10, Mughal (*India Office Library*)

With screams from all, except himself and the evil cat's
Head which jeered, and rejoined itself to the body
And said, "What was that intended to imply?"
"The true friend of cat," said the knight, "knows
That cat in ninety-nine which walks for women
And not for itself alone, the animal which is
The familiar of witches.
                              But it seems as if
I have not exorcised this particular one enough."

"You are remarkably right", said the reconstructured cat
Sapiently, "and for this wisdom you will wend,
By a promise you will here and now provide,
One year through numerous travails of the world and come
To the terrible temple of the great cat-goddess,
The mere pictures of whom inflict fevers and death
On the temerarious beholder who braves them,
Leading lady of many a lousy psychotropic
Trance. There we shall truly meet again,
And I shall take my turn."
                              So the seventh knight
Ground on grimly over the bogs and crags of the world
Lodging roughly, going rudely his slow way
On his bewildered horse through innumerable bleak,
Colourless, sleazy, subtopiate regions,
Demoralising tracts of megalosuburbia,
And came, just after eleven heavy months, to a splendid
Castle where he was welcomed very festively.
                                                    There,
In the course of after-dinner prattle of the price of property,
He thought he might try to elicit where the temple
Of the great cat-goddess stood, half-hoping it had not
Survived redevelopment.
                              "My fine fellow, I can
Tell you the lie of the land," said the lord his host,
But linger a day or two here, love, enjoy some relaxation"
—And his lady smiled in sly sympathy and accord—
"While I do some terribly tedious hunting. And, by the way,
Be good!"
              With an inward feeling of distant déjà vu,
The seventh knight agreed; and for three successive days,
Was allowed to lie lazily in bed while his host
Hunted and left his lady behind (just as he had read somewhere:
Because, to truncate a tangled tale,
Coming in sleek, scarlet, delightful garments,
She insisted on sleeping with him thoroughly each of the three

Days her husband was out happily hunting the evening meal,
Which the knight acquiesced in with an uneasy
Sense of compromise, and suspicion).
                              Each night, the master,
Hot and bothered, and scenting himself, brought back
The special spoils of a strenuous day in the field;
For this supper asking nothing in return and reward
But the knight's company in anecdotes and carousing;
And on the last day, as promised, he provided
Instructions for getting to the great cat-goddess' place.

It proved a daunting plod over muddy areas,
An extremely unclean excursion, so that when the knight
Arrived there, both he and his horse exhausted,
Spattered in the saddle from travel, he thought it was his tiredness
That stopped him from seeing where it was. But suddenly,
He saw it, a low brick thing nearly hidden in the grasses
Of a thistly field, with peculiar peep-holes from which
Any occupant, sitting in a safe nook, could
Scan out.
        Dismounting the knight called, clearly, and
Loudly as he was able, on whoever lurked inside to
Emerge, and there expeditiously appeared a
Truly tremendous cat, the size of a full-grown woman.
"As I promised and pledged I would do, in all duty,"
Stated the knight, "I have travelled to the temple
Of the great cat-goddess to pay the penalty for
Following up certain suspicions too rashly,
And acting in anger."
                    The vast cat mysteriously smiled,
Saying, "Listen. As an artful knight, you showed
Some shrewdness in discerning a witch's cat;
As a truly brave one you moved boldly
Against a defenceless, domestic animal; as
A plodder you showed some powerful persistence
In going your way through the world for a whole year
To find out this frightful place; as a seizer of chances
You lay three times with the lady of the castle,
Obviously not having offered any oath you would
Thereby break; thus, a clean code of knightly
Tactics you have most tightly kept, and
Will be rightly rewarded."
                        At which the vast beast
Cast off its outer cat-costume to step calmly
Forth as the seventh daughter, dressed in the delightful,
Scarlet, sleek garments of the mistress of the castle.

Superbia, Hieronymus Bosch (*Museo del Prado, Madrid*)

"I was," she said, "all the time secretly concealed
In the little anatomy of the cat, and in the body
Of the lady of the castle you came to know a bit,
And the knight of the castle, my master and lord,
Was all the time my own dear mother in drag.
So on the basis of all that you may bow, and beg now
The hand of the seventh daughter you came to collect.
There is no way out."

                So, haltingly heeding
These dreadful words, the dumbstruck fellow put
His proposals, too perplexed to do other, and the pair
Were rapidly wed. And they went on to work through
Many years of irrefrangible, retributive wedlock
(For she turned out termagant as well as witch)

—Yet concerning these travails I cannot, truthfully, say
I am sad or sorry, and I cannot make this knight an
Object of pity, because as a grown-up I genuinely regard
Knights and knighthood and weapons and the mores
Of a warrior society as both juvenile and degrading.

Tobermory

Saki

It was a chill, rain-washed afternoon of a late August day, that indefinite season when partridges are still in the security of cold storage, and there is nothing to hunt—unless one is bounded on the north by the Bristol Channel, in which case one may lawfully gallop after fat red stags. Lady Blemley's house-party was not bounded on the north by the Bristol Channel, hence there was a full gathering of her guests round the tea-table on this particular afternoon. And, in spite of the blankness of the season and the triteness of the occasion, there was no trace in the company of that fatigued restlessness which means a dread of the pianola and a subdued hankering for auction bridge. The undisguised, open-mouthed attention of the entire party was fixed on the homely, negative personality of Mr Cornelius Appin. Of all her guests, he was the one who had come to Lady Blemley with the vaguest reputation. Someone had said he was "clever", and he had got his invitation in the moderate expectation, on the part of his hostess, that some portion at least of his cleverness would be contributed to the general entertainment. Until tea-time that day she had been unable to discover in what direction, if any, his cleverness lay. He was neither a wit nor a croquet champion, a hypnotic force nor a begetter of amateur theatricals. Neither did his exterior suggest the sort of man in whom women are willing to pardon a generous measure of mental deficiency. He had subsided into mere Mr Appin, and the Cornelius seemed a piece of transparent baptismal bluff. And now he was claiming to have launched on the world a discovery beside which the invention of gun powder, of the printing-press, and of steam loco-motion were inconsiderable trifles. Science had made bewildering strides in many directions during recent decades, but this thing seemed to belong to the domain of miracle rather than to scientific achievement.

"And do you really ask us to believe," Sir Wilfrid was saying, "that you have discovered a means for instructing animals in the art of human speech, and that dear old Tobermory has proved your first successful pupil?"

"It is a problem at which I have worked for the last seventeen years," said Mr Appin, "but only during the last eight or nine months have I been rewarded with glimmerings of success. Of course I have experimented with thousands of animals, but latterly only with cats, those wonder-ful creatures which have assimilated themselves so marvellously with our civilisation while retaining all their highly developed feral instincts. Here and there among cats one comes across an outstanding superior intellect, just as one does among the ruck of human beings, and when I made the acquaintance of Tobermory a week ago I saw at once that I was in contact with a 'Beyond-cat' of extraordinary intelligence. I had gone far along the road to success in recent experiments; with Tobermory, as you call him, I have reached the goal."

Mr Appin concluded his remarkable statement in a voice which he strove to divest of a triumphant inflexion. No one said "Rats", though Clovis's lips moved in a monosyllabic contortion which probably invoked those rodents of disbelief.

The Cat, Bart A. van der Leck (*Rijksmuseum Kröller-Müller, Otterlo*)

"And do you mean to say," asked Miss Resker, after a slight pause, "that you have taught Tobermory to say and understand easy sentences of one syllable?"

"My dear Miss Resker," said the wonder-worker patiently, "one teaches little children and savages and backward adults in that piecemeal fashion; when one has once solved the problem of making a beginning with an animal of highly developed intelligence one has no need for those halting methods. Tobermory can speak our language with perfect correctness."

This time Clovis very distinctly said, "Beyond-rats!" Sir Wilfrid was more polite, but equally sceptical.

"Hadn't we better have the cat in and judge for ourselves?" suggested Lady Blemley.

Sir Wilfrid went in search of the animal, and the company settled themselves down to the languid expectation of witnessing some more or less adroit drawing-room ventriloquism.

In a minute Sir Wilfrid was back in the room, his face white beneath its tan and his eyes dilated with excitement.

"By Gad, it's true!"

His agitation was unmistakably genuine, and his hearers started forward in a thrill of awakened interest.

Collapsing into an armchair he continued breathlessly; "I found him dozing in the smoking-room, and called after him to come for his tea. He blinked at me in his usual way, and I said, 'Come on, Toby; don't keep us waiting;' and, by Gad! he drawled out in a most horribly natural voice, that he'd come when he dashed well pleased! I nearly jumped out of my skin!"

Appin had preached to absolutely incredulous hearers; Sir Wilfrid's statement carried instant conviction. A Babel-like chorus of startled exclamation arose, amid which the scientist sat mutely enjoying the first fruit of his stupendous discovery.

In the midst of the clamour Tobermory entered the room and made his way with velvet tread and studied unconcern across to the group seated round the tea-table.

A sudden hush of awkwardness and constraint fell on the company. Somehow there seemed an element of embarrassment in addressing on equal terms a domestic cat of acknowledged mental ability.

"Will you have some milk, Tobermory?" asked Lady Blemley in a rather strained voice.

"I don't mind if I do," was the response, couched in a tone of even indifference. A shiver of suppressed excitement went through the listeners, and Lady Blemley might be excused for pouring out the saucerful of milk rather unsteadily.

"I am afraid I have spilled a good deal of it,' she said apologetically.

"After all, it's not my Axminster," was Tobermory's rejoinder.

Another silence fell on the group, and then Miss Resker, in her best district-visitor manner, asked if the human language had been difficult to learn. Tobermory looked squarely at her for a moment and then fixed his gaze serenely on the middle distance. It was obvious that boring questions lay outside his scheme of life.

"What do you think of human intelligence?" asked Mavis Pellington lamely.

"Of whose intelligence in particular?" asked Tobermory coldly.

"Oh, well, mine for instance," said Mavis, with a feeble laugh.

"You put me in an embarrassing position," said Tobermory, whose tone and attitude certainly did not suggest a shred of embarrassment. "When your inclusion in this house party was suggested, Sir Wilfrid protested that you were the most brainless woman of his acquaintance, and that there was a wide distinction between hospitality and the care of the feeble-minded. Lady Blemley replied that your lack of brain-power was the precise quality which had earned you your invitation, as you were the only person she could think of who might be idiotic enough to buy their old car. You know, the one they call 'The Envy of Sisyphus', because it goes quite nicely uphill if you push it."

Lady Blemley's protestations would have had greater effect if she had not casually suggested to Mavis only that morning that the car in question would be just the thing for her down at her Devonshire home.

Major Barfield plunged in heavily to effect a diversion.

"How about your carryings-on with the tortoiseshell puss up at the stables, eh?"

The moment he had said it everyone realised the blunder.

"One does not usually discuss these matters in public," said Tobermory frigidly. "From a slight observation of your ways since you've been in this house I should imagine you'd find it inconvenient if I were to shift the conversation on to your own little affairs."

The panic which ensued was not confined to the Major.

"Would you like to go and see if cook has got your dinner ready?" suggested Lady Blemley hurriedly, affecting to ignore the fact that it wanted at least two hours to Tobermory's dinner-time.

"Thanks," said Tobermory, "not quite so soon after my tea. I don't want to die of indigestion."

"Cats have nine lives, you know," said Sir Wilfrid heartily.

"Possibly," answered Tobermory; "but only one liver."

"Adelaide!" said Mrs Cornett, "do you mean to encourage that cat to go out and gossip about us in the servants' hall?"

Proverb, XVIIth century, Flemish (*Musée du Berry, Bourges*)

The panic had indeed become general. A narrow ornamental balustrade ran in front of most of the bedroom windows at the Towers, and it was recalled with dismay that this had formed a favourite promenade for Tobermory at all hours, whence he could watch the pigeons—and heaven knew what else besides. If he intended to become reminiscent in his present outspoken strain the effect would be something more than disconcerting. Mrs Cornett, who spent much time at her toilet table, and whose complexion was reputed to be of a nomadic though punctual disposition, looked as ill at ease as the Major. Miss Scrawen, who wrote fiercely sensuous poetry and led a blameless life, merely displayed irritation; if you are methodical and virtuous in private you don't necessarily want everyone to know it. Bertie van Tahn, who was so depraved at seventeen that he had long ago given up trying to be any worse, turned a dull shade of gardenia white, but he did not commit the error of dashing out of the room like Odo Finsberry, a young gentleman who was understood to be reading for the Church and who was possibly disturbed at the thought of scandals he might hear concerning other people. Clovis had the presence of mind to maintain a composed exterior; privately he was calculating how long it would take to procure a box of fancy mice through the agency of the *Exchange and Mart* as a species of hush-money.

Even in a delicate situation like the present, Agnes Resker could not endure to remain too long in the background.

"Why did I ever come down here?" she asked dramatically. Tobermory immediately accepted the opening.

"Judging by what you said to Mrs Cornett on the croquet lawn yesterday, you were out for food. You described the Blemleys as the dullest people to stay with that you knew, but said they were clever enough to employ a first-rate cook; otherwise they'd find it difficult to get anyone to come down a second time."

"There's not a word of truth in it! I appeal to Mrs Cornett—" exclaimed the discomfitted Agnes.

"Mrs Cornett repeated your remark afterwards to Bertie van Tahn," continued Tobermory, "and said, 'That woman is a regular Hunger Marcher; she'd go anywhere for four square meals a day,' and Bertie van Tahn said—"

At this point the chronicle mercifully ceased. Tobermory had caught a glimpse of the big yellow Tom from the Rectory working his way through the shrubbery towards the stable wing. In a flash he had vanished through the open French window.

With the disappearance of his too brilliant pupil Cornelius Appin found himself beset by a hurricane of bitter upbraiding, anxious inquiry, and frightened entreaty. The responsibility for the situation lay with him, and he must prevent matters from becoming worse. Could Tobermory impart his dangerous gift to other cats? was the first question he had to answer. It was possible, he replied, that he might have initiated his intimate friend the stable puss into his new accomplishment, but it was unlikely that his teaching could have taken a wider range as yet.

"Then," said Mrs Cornett, "Tobermory may be a valuable cat and a great pet; but I'm sure you'll agree, Adelaide, that both he and the stable cat must be done away with without delay."

"You don't suppose I've enjoyed the last quarter of an hour, do you?" said Lady Blemley bitterly. "My husband and I are very fond of Tobermory—at least, we were before this horrible accomplishment was infused into him; but now, of course, the only thing is to have him destroyed as soon as possible."

"We can put some strychnine in the scraps he always gets at dinner-time," said Sir Wilfrid, "and I will go and drown the stable cat myself. The coachman will be very sore at losing his pet,

Apollo Killing the Cyclops (detail), Domenichino (*National Gallery, London*)

but I'll say a very catching form of mange has broken out in both cats and we're afraid of it spreading to the kennels."

"But my great discovery!" expostulated Mr Appin; "after all my years of research and experiment—"

"You can go and experiment on the short-horns at the farm, who are under proper control," said Mrs Cornett, "or the elephants at the Zoological Gardens. They're said to be highly intelligent, and they have this recommendation, that they don't come creeping about our bedrooms and under chairs, and so forth."

An archangel ecstatically proclaiming the Millennium, and then finding that it clashed unpardonably with Henley and would have to be indefinitely postponed, could hardly have felt more crestfallen than Cornelius Appin at the reception of his wonderful achievements. Public opinion, however, was against him—in fact, had the general voice been consulted on the subject it is probable that a strong minority vote would have been in favour of including him in the strychnine diet.

Defective train arrangements and a nervous desire to see matters brought to a finish prevented an immediate dispersal of the party, but dinner that evening was not a social success. Sir Wilfrid had had rather a trying time with the stable cat and subsequently with the coachman. Agnes Resker ostentatiously limited her repast to a morsel of dry toast, which she bit as though it were a personal enemy, while Mavis Pellington maintained a vindictive silence throughout the meal. Lady Blemley kept up a flow of what she hoped was conversation, but her attention was fixed on the doorway. A plateful of carefully dosed fish scraps was in readiness on the sideboard, but sweets and savoury and dessert went their way, and no Tobermory appeared either in the dining-room or kitchen.

The sepulchral dinner was cheerful compared with the subsequent vigil in the smoking-room. Eating and drinking had at least supplied a distraction and cloak to the prevailing embarrassment. Bridge was out of the question in the general tension of nerves and tempers, and after Odo Finsberry had given a lugubrious rendering of "Melisande in the Wood" to a frigid audience, music was tacitly avoided. At eleven the servants went to bed, announcing that the small window in the pantry had been left open as usual for Tobermory's private use. The guests read steadily through the current batch of magazines, and fell back gradually on the "Badminton Library" and bound volumes of *Punch*. Lady Blemley made periodic visits to the pantry, returning each time with an expression of listless depression which forestalled questioning.

At two o'clock Clovis broke the dominating silence.

"He won't turn up to-night. He's probably in the local newspaper office at the present moment, dictating the first instalment of his reminiscences. Lady What's-her-name's book won't be in it. It will be the event of the day."

Having made this contribution to the general cheerfulness, Clovis went to bed. At long intervals the various members of the house party followed his example.

The servants taking round the early tea made a uniform announcement in reply to a uniform question. Tobermory had not returned.

Breakfast was, if anything, a more unpleasant function than dinner had been, but before its conclusion the situation was relieved. Tobermory's corpse was brought in from the shrubbery, where a gardener had just discovered it. From the bites on his throat and the yellow fur which coated his claws it was evident that he had fallen in unequal combat with the big Tom from the Rectory.

By midday most of the guests had quitted the Towers, and after lunch Lady Blemley had sufficiently recovered her spirits to write an extremely nasty letter to the Rectory about the loss of her valuable pet.

Tobermory had been Appin's one successful pupil, and he was destined to have no successor. A few weeks later an elephant in the Dresden Zoological Garden, which had shown no previous signs of irritability, broke loose and killed an Englishman who had apparently been teasing it. The victim's name was variously reported in the papers as Oppin and Eppelin, but his front name was faithfully rendered Cornelius.

"If he was trying German irregular verbs on the poor beast," said Clovis, "he deserved all he got."

The Singing Cat

Stevie Smith

It was a little captive cat
  Upon a crowded train
His mistress takes him from his box
  To ease his fretful pain.

She holds him tight upon her knee
  The graceful animal
And all the people look at him
  He is so beautiful.

But oh he pricks and oh he prods
  And turns upon her knee
Then lifteth up his innocent voice
  In plaintive melody.

He lifteth up his innocent voice
  He lifteth up, he singeth
And to each human countenance
  A smile of grace he bringeth.

He lifteth up his innocent paw
  Upon her breast he clingeth
And everybody cries, Behold
  The cat, the cat that singeth.

He lifteth up his innocent voice
  He lifteth up, he singeth
And all the people warm themselves
  In the love his beauty bringeth.

A Girl with a Kitten, Jean-Baptiste Perronneau (*National Gallery, London*)

"When In Doubt—Wash"

Paul Gallico

These extracts are taken, with the author's permission, from Jennie, *by Paul Gallico. At the beginning of the adventure, Peter the boy turned into a white cat, is thrown out to shift for himself in London. Hounded and pursued from the West End to the Docks, he is half-killed by a tough tom cat, and his life is only saved when Jennie, a stray London tabby, who lives in a dockside warehouse, finds him unconscious in the street and drags him into her hideout.*

"'When in doubt—any kind of doubt—*Wash!*' That is Rule No. 1," said Jennie. She sat now primly and a little stiffly, with her tail wrapped around her feet, near the head of the big bed beneath the Napoleon Initial and Crown, rather like a schoolmistress. But it was obvious that the role of teacher and the respectful attention Peter bestowed upon her were not unendurable, because she had a pleased expression and her eyes were again gleaming brightly.

The sun had reached its noon zenith in the sky in the world that lay outside the dark and grimy warehouse, and coming in slantwise through the small window sent a dusty shaft that fell like a theatrical spotlight about Jennie's head and shoulders as she lectured.

"If you have committed any kind of an error and anyone scolds you—wash," she was saying.

A Farmyard Cat (Pictorial Press Ltd)

[158]

"If you slip and fall off something and somebody laughs at you—wash. If you are getting the worst of an argument and want to break off hostilities until you have composed yourself, start washing. Remember, *every* cat respects another cat at her toilet. That's our first rule of social deportment, and you must also observe it.

"Whatever the situation, whatever difficulty you may be in, you can't go wrong if you wash. If you come into a room full of people you do not know, and who are confusing to you, sit right down in the midst of them and start washing. They'll end up by quieting down and watching you. Some noise frightens *you* into a jump, and somebody you know saw you were frightened—begin washing immediately.

"If somebody calls you and you don't care to come and still you don't wish to make it a direct insult—wash. If you've started off to go somewhere and suddenly can't remember where it was you wanted to go, sit right down and begin brushing up a little. It will come back to you. Something hurt you? Wash it. Tired of playing with someone who has been kind enough to take time and trouble and you want to break off without hurting his or her feelings—start washing.

"Oh, there are dozens of things! Door closed and you're burning up because no one will open it for you—have yourself a little wash and forget it. Somebody petting another cat or dog in the same room, and you are annoyed over *that*—be nonchalant; wash. Feel sad—wash away your blues. Been picked up by somebody you don't particularly fancy and who didn't smell good—wash him off immediately and pointedly where he can see you do it. Overcome by emotion—a wash will help you to get a grip on yourself again. Any time, anyhow, in any manner, for whatever purpose, wherever you are, whenever and why ever that you want to clear the air, or get a moment's respite or think things over—WASH!

"And," concluded Jennie, drawing a long breath, "of course you also wash to get clean and to keep clean."

"Goodness!" said Peter, quite worried. "I don't see how I could possibly remember them all."

"You don't have to remember any of it, actually," Jennie explained. "All that you have to remember is Rule 1: 'When in doubt—WASH!'"

Peter, who, like all boys, had no objection to being reasonably clean, but not *too* clean, saw the problem of washing looming up large and threatening to occupy all of his time. "It's true, I remember, you always do seem to be washing," he protested to Jennie. "I mean, all cats I've seen, but I don't see why. Why do cats spend so much of their time at it?"

Jennie considered his question for a moment, and then replied, "Because it feels so good to be clean."

"Well, at any rate I shall never be capable of doing it," Peter remarked, "because I won't be able to reach places now that I am a cat and cannot use my hands. And even when I was a boy, Nanny used to have to wash my back for me . . ."

"Nothing of the kind," said Jennie. "The first thing you will learn that there isn't an inch of herself or himself that a cat cannot reach to wash. If you had ever owned one of us, you would know. Now watch me. We'll begin with the back. I'll do it first, and then you come over here alongside of me and do as I do."

And thereupon sitting upright, she turned her head around over her shoulder with a wonderful ease and grace, using little short strokes of her tongue and keeping her chin down close to her body, she began to wash over and around her left shoulder-blade, gradually increasing the amount of turn and the length of the stroking movement of her head until her rough, pink tongue was travelling smoothly and firmly along the region of her upper spine.

"Oh, I never could!" cried Peter, "because I cannot twist my head around as far as you can.

I never know what is going on behind me unless I turn right around."

"Try," was all Jennie replied.

Peter did, and to his astonishment found that whereas when he had been a boy he had been unable to turn his head more left and right than barely to be able to look over his shoulders, now he could swivel it quite around on his neck so that he was actually gazing out behind him. And when he stuck out his tongue and moved his head in small circles as he had seen Jennie do, there he was washing around his left shoulder.

"Oh, bravo! Splendid!" applauded Jennie. "There, you see! Well done, Peter. Now turn a little more—you're bound to be a bit stiff at first—and down the spine you go!"

And indeed, down the spine, about half-way from below his neck to the middle of his back, Peter went. He was so delighted that he tried to purr and wash at the same time, and actually achieved it.

"Now," Jennie coached, "for the rest of the way down, you can help yourself and make it easier—like this. Curve your body around and go a little lower so that you are half-sitting, half-lying. That's it! Brace yourself against your right paw and pull your left paw in a little closer to you so that it is out of the way. There . . . Now, you see, that brings the rest of you nicely around in a curve where you can get at it. Finish off the left side of your back and hind-quarters and then shift around and do the other side."

Peter did so, and was amazed to find with what little effort the whole of his spine and hind-quarters was brought within ample reach of his busy tongue. He even essayed to have a go at his tail from this position, but found this a more elusive customer. It would keep squirming away.

Jennie smiled. "Try putting a paw on it to hold it down. The right one. You can still brace yourself with it. That's it. We'll get at the underside of it later on."

Peter was so enchanted with what he had learned that he would have gone on washing and washing the two sides of his back and his flanks and quarters if Jennie hadn't said, "There, that's enough of that. There's still plenty left, you know. Now you must do your front and the stomach and the inside of your paws and quarters."

The front limbs and paws, of course, proved easy for Peter, for they were quite close, but when he attempted to tackle his chest, it was something else.

"Try lying down first," Jennie suggested. "After a while you'll get so supple you will be able to wash your chest sitting up just by sticking your tongue out a little more and bobbing your head. But it's easier lying down on your side. Here, like this," and she suited the action to the word, and soon Peter found that he actually was succeeding in washing his chest-fur just beneath his chin.

"But I can't get at my middle," he complained, for indeed the underside of his belly defied his clumsy attempts to reach it, bend and twist as he would.

Jennie smiled. "'*Can't* catches no mice'," she quoted. "That is more difficult. Watch me now. You won't do it lying on your side. Sit up a bit and rock on your tail. That's it, get your tail right under you. You can brace with either of your forepaws, or both. Now, you see, that bends you right around again and brings your stomach within reach. You'll get it with practice. It's all curves. That's why we were made that way."

Peter found it more awkward to balance than in the other position and fell over several times, but soon found that he was getting better at it and that each portion of his person that was thus made accessible to him through Jennie's knowledge, experience and teaching brought him a new enjoyment and pleasure of accomplishment. And, of course, Jennie's approval made him very proud.

He was forging ahead so rapidly with his lesson that he decided to see whether he could go

Simpkin Housekeeping, Beatrix Potter (*Tate Gallery, London*)

and learn by himself. "Now how would you go about doing the inside of the hind-quarter?" she asked.

"Oh, that's easy," Peter cried. But it wasn't at all. In fact, the more he tried and strained and reached and curved, the further away did his hind leg seem to go. He tried first the right and then the left, and finally got himself tangled in such a heap of legs, paws and tail that he fell right over in a manner that Jennie had to take a few quick dabs at herself to keep from laughing.

"I can't—I mean, I don't see how . . ." wailed Peter, "there isn't any way . . ."

Jenny was contrite at once and hoped Peter had not seen she had been amused. "Oh, I'm sorry," she declared. "That wasn't fair of me. There is, but it's most difficult, and you have to know how. It took me the longest time when my mother tried to show me. Here, does this suggest anything to you—Leg of Mutton? I'm sure you've seen it dozens of times," and she assumed an odd position with her right leg sticking straight up in the air and somehow close to her head, almost like the contortionist that Peter had seen at the circus at Olympia who had twisted himself right around so that his head came down between his legs. He was sure that he could never do it.

Peter tried to imitate Jennie, but only succeeded in winding himself into a worse knot. Jennie came to his rescue once more. "See here," she said, "let's try it by counts, one stage at a time. Once you've done it, you know, you'll never forget it. Now——

[161]

"One—rock on your tail." Peter rocked.

"Two—brace yourself with your left forepaw." Peter braced.

"Three—half-sit, and bend your back." Peter managed that, and made himself into the letter C.

"Four—stretch out the left leg all the way. That will keep you from falling over the other side and provide a balance for the paw to push against." This, too, worked out exactly as Jennie described it when Peter tried it.

"Five—swing your right leg from the hip—you'll find it will go—with the foot pointing straight up into the air. Yes, like that, but *outside*, not inside the right forepaw." It went better this time. Peter got it almost up.

"Six—N O W you've got it. Hold yourself steady by bracing the right front forepaw. S O !"

Peter felt like shouting with joy. For there he was, actually sitting, leg of mutton, his hind-quarter shooting up right past his cheek and the whole inside of his leg exposed. He felt that he was really doubled back on himself like the contortionist, and he wished that Nanny were there so that he could show her.

By twisting and turning a little, there was no part of him underneath that he could not reach, and he washed first one side and then, without any further instruction from Jennie managed to reverse the position and get the left leg up, which drew forth an admiring "Oh, you are clever!" from Jennie—"it took me just ages to learn to work the left side. It all depends whether you are left or right pawed, but you caught on to it immediately. Now there's only one thing more. The back of the neck, the ears and the face."

In a rush to earn more praise Peter went nearly cross-eyed trying to get his tongue out and around to reach behind him and on top of him, and of course it wouldn't work. He cried, "Oh, dear, T H A T must be the most complicated of all."

"On the contrary," smiled Jennie, "it's quite the simplest. Wet the side of your front paw." Peter did so. "Now rub it around over your ears and the back of your neck."

Now it was Peter's turn to laugh at himself. "How stupid I am," he said. "That part is just the way I do it at home. Except I use a flannel, and Nanny stands there watching to make certain I go behind the ears."

"Well," said Jennie, "*I'm* watching you now . . ."

So Peter completed his bath by wetting one paw and then the other, on the side and in the middle on the pads, and washing first his ears, then both sides of his face, the back of his neck, his whiskers, and even a little under his chin, and over his nose and eyes.

And now he found that having washed himself all over, from head to foot, the most wonderful feeling of comfort and relaxation had come over him. It was quite a different sensation from the time that Jennie had washed him and which had somehow taken him back to the days when he was very little and his mother was looking after him.

This time he felt a kind of glow in his skin and a sense of well-being in his muscles as though every one of them had been properly used and stretched. In the light from the last of the shaft of the sun that was just passing from the window of the store-house he could see how his white fur glistened from the treatment he had given it, as smooth as silk and as soft.

Peter felt a delicious drowsiness. His eyes began to close, and as from a distance he heard Jennie say "It's good to take a nap after washing. I always do. You've earned it."

Just before he dropped off to sleep, Peter felt her curl up against him, her back touching his, warm and secure, and the next moment he was off in sweet and dreamless slumber.

"I'm awfully thirsty, Jennie," Peter whispered.

Two Men and Four Cats, Jean-Antoine Watteau (*Musée Bonnat, Bayonne*)

They had been crouching there around the bend of the warehouse corridor for the better part of an hour waiting for the men to finish the work of carrying out the furniture from the storage bin.

Jennie flattened herself and peered around the corner. "Soon," she said. "There are only a few pieces left."

"How I wish I had a tall, cool glass of milk," Peter said.

Jennie turned her head and looked at him. "Dish of milk, you mean. You wouldn't be able to drink it out of a glass. And as for milk—do you know how long it is since I have seen or tasted milk? In our kind of life, I mean, cut off from humans, there isn't any milk. If you're thirsty you find some rain-water or some slops in the gutter or in a pail left out, or you can go down the stone steps to the river landings when they are deserted at night, if you don't mind your water a little oily and brackish."

Peter was not at all pleased with the prospect and he had not yet got used to the fact that he was no longer a boy, with a home and family, but a white cat with no home at all and no one to befriend him but another scrawny stray.

He was so desperately thirsty and the picture drawn by Jennie so gloomy and unpleasant that he could not help bursting into tears and crying. "But I'm *used* to milk! I like it, and Nanny gives me some every day . . ."

[163]

"Sshhh!" cautioned Jennie, "they'll hear you." Then she added: "There's nobody goes about setting out dishes of milk for strays. You'll get used to not having it eventually."

But Peter didn't think so, and continued to cry softly to himself while Jennie Baldrin watched him with growing concern and bewilderment. She seemed to be trying to make up her mind about something which apparently she did not very much wish to do. But finally, when it appeared that she could bear his unhappiness no longer, she whispered to him "Come, now . . . don't take on so! I know a place where I think I can get you a dish of milk. We'll go there."

The thought caused Peter to stop crying and brighten up immediately. "Yes?" he said. "Where?"

"There's an old watchman lives in a shack down by the tea docks," Jennie told him. "He's lonely, likes cats, and is always good for a titbit, especially for me. He's been after me to come and live with him for months. Of course, I wouldn't dream of it."

"But," said Peter, not wishing to argue himself out of milk but only desiring to understand clearly the terms under which they were to have it, "that *is* taking it from people, isn't it?"

"It's taking, but not *giving* anything," Jennie said, with that strange, unhappy intenseness that came over her whenever she discussed anything to do with human beings. "We'll *have it* and then walk out on him."

"Would that be right?" Peter asked. It slipped out almost before he was aware of it, for he very much wanted the milk and he equally did not wish to offend Jennie. But it was just that he had been taught certain ways of behaviour, or felt them to be so by instinct, and this seemed a poor way of repaying a kindness. Clearly he had somewhat put Jennie out, for she stiffened slightly and with the nearest thing to a cold look she had bestowed upon him since they had met, said "You can't have it both ways, Peter. If you want to live my kind of life, and I can't see where you have very much choice at the moment——"

"But of course I do!" Peter hastened to explain, "it's just that I'm not yet quite familiar with the different way cats feel than the way people feel. And I will do as you say, and I do want to learn . . ."

From her expression, Jennie did not appear to be too pleased with this speech either, but before she could remark upon it there came a loud call from the movers, "That's the lot, then," and another voice replied, "Righty-ho!" Jennie peered around the corner and said, "They've finished. We'll wait a few minutes to make sure they don't come back, and then we'll start."

When they were certain that the aisle was quite deserted again, they set off, Jennie leading, past the empty bin and down the corridor in the direction the men had taken, but before they had gone very far Jennie branched off to the right on a new track until she came to a bin close to the outside wall of the warehouse, filled with horrible, new, modern kind of furniture, chrome-bound leather and overstuffed plush. She led Peter to the back where there was a good-sized hole in the baseboard. It looked dark and forbidding inside.

"Don't be afraid," Jennie said. "Just follow me. We go to the right and then to the left, but it gets light very quickly."

She slipped in with Peter after her, and it soon grew pitch black. Peter now discovered that he was feeling through the ends of his whiskers, rather than seeing where Jennie was, and he had no difficulty in following her, particularly inasmuch as it soon became bright enough to see that they were in a tunnel through which a large iron pipe more than a foot in diameter was running. Then Peter saw where the light was coming from. There was a hole in the pipe where it had rusted through a few feet from where it gave exit to the street.

Apparently the pipe was used as some kind of air intake, or had something to do with the ventilation of the warehouse, for it had once had a grating over the end of it, but the fastenings of that had long since rusted and it had fallen away, and there was nothing to bar their way out.

Peter was so pleased and excited at the prospect of seeing the sun and being out of doors again that he hurried past Jennie and would have rushed out into the street had not the alarm in her warning cry checked him just before he emerged from the opening.

"Peter! Wait!" she cried. "Not like that! Cats never, *never* rush out from places. Don't you know about Pausing on the Threshold, or Lingering on the Sill? But then, of course, you wouldn't. Oh, dear, I don't mean always to be telling you what to do and what not to do, but this is really Important. It's almost Lesson No. 2. You never hurry out of any place, and particularly not outdoors."

Cat, photo Will Green

Peter saw that Jennie had quite recovered her good nature and apparently had forgotten that she had been upset with him. He was curious to find out the reasons for her warning. He said "I don't quite understand, Jennie. You mean, I'm not to stop before coming in, but I am whenever I go out?"

"Of course. What else?" replied Jennie, sitting down quite calmly in the mouth of the exit and showing not the slightest disposition to go through it and into the street. "You know what's inside because you come from there. You don't know what's outside because you haven't been there. That's common ordinary sense for anyone, I should think."

"Yes, but what is there outside to be afraid of, really?" inquired Peter. "I mean, after all, if you know where you live and the street and houses and all which don't change——"

"Oh, my goodness," said Jennie. "I couldn't try to tell you them all. To begin with—dogs, people, moving vehicles, the weather and changes in temperature, the condition of the street, is it wet or dry, clean or dirty, what has been left lying about, what is parked at the kerb, and whether anybody is coming along, on which side of the street and in how much of a hurry.

"And it isn't that you're actually afraid. It's just that you want to *know*. And you ought to know, if you have your wits about you, everything your eyes, your ears, your nose and the ends of your whiskers can tell you. And so you stop, look, listen, and *feel*. We have a saying: 'Heaven is over-crowded with kittens who rushed out of doors without first stopping and *receiving* a little.'

"There might be another cat in the vicinity, bent on mischief, or looking for a fight. You'd certainly want to know about that before you stepped out into something you weren't prepared for. Then you'd want to know all about the weather, not only what it's like at the moment, but but what it's going to be doing later, say an hour from then. If it's going to come on to rain or thunder, you wouldn't want to be too far from home. Your whiskers and your skin tell you that.

"And then, anyway," Jennie concluded, "it's a good idea on general principles not to rush into things. When you go out there are very few places to go to that won't be there just the same five minutes later, and the chances of your getting there will be ever so much better. Come here and squat down beside me and we'll just have a look."

Peter did as she suggested and lay down directly in the opening with his paws tucked under him, and felt quite natural doing it, and suddenly he was glad that Jennie had stopped him and that he hadn't gone charging out into goodness knows what.

Feet went by at intervals. By observation he got to know something about the size of the shoes, which were mostly the heavy boots belonging to workmen, their speed, and how near they came to the wall of the warehouse. The wheeled traffic was of the heavy type—huge horse-drawn drays, and motor lorries that rumbled past ominously loud, and the horses' feet, huge things with big, shaggy fetlocks were another danger. Far in the distance, Peter heard Big Ben strike four. The sound would not have reached him as a human being, perhaps, but it travelled all the distance from the Houses of Parliament to his cat's ears and informed him of the time.

Now he used his nostrils and sniffed the scents that came to his nose and tried to understand what they told him. There was a strong smell of tea and a queer odour that he could not identify, he just knew he didn't like it. He recognised dry goods, machinery, musk and spices, and horses and burned petrol, exhaust gases, tar and soft coal smoke, the kind that comes from railway engines.

Jennie had got up now and was standing on the edge of the opening with only her head out, whiskers extended forward, quivering a little, and making small wrinkly movements with her nose. After a moment or so of this she turned to Peter quite relaxed and said "All clear. We can go now. No cats around. There's a dog been by, but only a mangy cur probably scared of his own shadow. There's a tea-boat just docked. That's good. The Watchman won't really have any responsibilities until she's unloaded. Rain's all cleared away. Probably won't rain for at least another forty-eight hours. Goods train just gone down into the docks area. That's fine. Means the gates'll be open, and besides, we can use the wagons for cover."

"Goodness!" Peter marvelled. "I don't see how you can tell all that from just one tiny sniff around. Do you suppose I'll ever——?"

"Of course you will," Jennie laughed, and with a bit of a purr added, "It's only a matter of getting used to it and looking at things the way a cat would. It's really nothing." And here she gave herself two or three self-conscious licks, for, truth to tell, she was just a trifle vain and nothing delighted her so much as to appear clever in Peter's eyes, which was only feline.

"Well, I don't understand——" Peter began, saying just the right thing and giving her the lead which she was quick to take up.

"It's really quite simple," she explained. "For instance, you can smell the tea. Well, that wasn't around last time I was outside. Means a tea-boat has come in and they've opened the hatches. No cats about—I don't get any signals on my receiver, at least not hostile ones. The dog that went by, well, goodness knows, you can smell *him*. If he had any class or self-respect that

Cat and Mouse, James Lloyd (*Tate Gallery, London*)

Inlaid choir stall (detail), Fra Raffaele de Brescia (*Monte Oliveto Maggiore, Siena*)

might lead him to chase cats, he'd be clean, and a clean dog smells different. This one was filthy, and that's why I say he's nothing to worry about. He'll be slinking along down back alleys and glad to be left alone. And as for the goods train that went by, after you get to know the neighbourhood it'll be easy for you too. You see, the smoke smell comes from the left, down where the docks are, so of course it went that way. And you know it was a goods train, because you can smell everything that was in the wagons. There, you see how easy it is?"

Peter again said the right thing, for he was learning how to please Jennie. "I think you're *enormously* clever," he told her. Her purr almost drowned out the sound of a passing horse-drawn dray. Then she cried to him gaily, "Come along, Peter! We're off!" and the two friends went out into the cobbled street.

Cat and Dog Merchant, Paris 1774

Macavity: The Mystery Cat

T. S. Eliot

Macavity's a Mystery Cat: he's called the Hidden Paw—
For he's the master criminal who can defy the Law.
He's the bafflement of Scotland Yard, the Flying Squad's despair:
For when they reach the scene of crime—*Macavity's not there*!

Macavity, Macavity, there's no one like Macavity,
He's broken every human law, he breaks the law of gravity.
His powers of levitation would make a fakir stare,
And when you reach the scene of crime—*Macavity's not there*!
You may seek him in the basement, you may look up in the air—
But I tell you once and once again, *Macavity's not there*!

Macavity's a ginger cat, he's very tall and thin;
You would know him if you saw him, for his eyes are sunken in.
His brow is deeply lined with thought, his head is highly domed;
His coat is dusty from neglect, his whiskers are uncombed.
He sways his head from side to side, with movements like a snake;
And when you think he's half asleep, he's always wide awake.

Macavity, Macavity, there's no one like Macavity,
For he's a fiend in feline shape, a monster of depravity.
You may meet him in a by-street, you may see him in the square—
But when a crime's discovered, then *Macavity's not there*!

He's outwardly respectable. (They say he cheats at cards.)
And his footprints are not found in any file of Scotland Yard's.
And when the larder's looted, or the jewel-case is rifled,
Or when the milk is missing, or another Peke's been stifled,
Or the greenhouse glass is broken, and the trellis past repair—
Ay, there's the wonder of the thing! *Macavity's not there*!

And when the Foreign Office find a Treaty's gone astray,
Or the Admiralty lose some plans and drawings by the way,
There may be a scrap of paper in the hall or on the stair—
But it's useless to investigate—*Macavity's not there*!
And when the loss has been disclosed, the Secret Service say:

"It *must* have been Macavity!"—but he's a mile away.
You'll be sure to find him resting, or a-licking of his thumbs,
Or engaged in doing complicated long division sums.

Macavity, Macavity, there's no one like Macavity,
There never was a Cat of such deceitfulness and suavity.
He always has an alibi, and one or two to spare:
At whatever time the deed took place—MACAVITY WASN'T THERE!
And they say that all the Cats whose wicked deeds are widely known
(I might mention Mungojerrie, I might mention Griddlebone)
Are nothing more than agents for the Cat who all the time
Just controls their operations: the Napoleon of Crime!

Pole Cat, photo S. C. Reynolds (*Pictorial Press Ltd*)

The Latecomer, Louis Wain (*Michael Parkin Fine Art Ltd*)

VI

 Cat's Killings

Growltiger's Last Stand

T. S. Eliot

Growltiger was a Bravo Cat, who travelled on a barge:
In fact he was the roughest cat that ever roamed at large.
From Gravesend up to Oxford he pursued his evil aims,
Rejoicing in his title of "The Terror of the Thames".

His manners and appearance did not calculate to please;
His coat was torn and seedy, he was baggy at the knees;
One ear was somewhat missing, no need to tell you why,
And he scowled upon a hostile world from one forbidding eye.

The cottagers of Rotherhithe knew something of his fame;
At Hammersmith and Putney people shuddered at his name.
They would fortify the hen-house, lock up the silly goose,
When the rumour ran along the shore: GROWLTIGER'S ON THE LOOSE!

Woe to the weak canary, that fluttered from its cage;
Woe to the pampered Pekinese, that faced Growltiger's rage;
Woe to the bristly Bandicoot, that lurks on foreign ships,
And woe to any Cat with whom Growltiger came to grips!

But most to Cats of foreign race his hatred had been vowed;
To Cats of foreign name and race no quarter was allowed.
The Persian and the Siamese regarded him with fear—
Because it was a Siamese had mauled his missing ear.

Now on a peaceful summer night, all nature seemed at play,
The tender moon was shining bright, the barge at Molesey lay.
All in the balmy moonlight it lay rocking on the tide—
And Growltiger was disposed to show his sentimental side.

His bucko mate, GRUMBUSKIN, long since had disappeared,
For to the Bell Hampton he had gone to wet his beard;
And his bosun, TUMBLEBRUTUS he too had stol'n away—
In the yard behind the Lion he was prowling for his prey.

The Cat and the Old Rat, Gustavé Dore

In the forepeak of the vessel Growltiger sate alone,
Concentrating his attention on the Lady GRIDDLEBONE.
And his raffish crew were sleeping in their barrels and their bunks—
As the Siamese came creeping in their sampans and their junks.

Growltiger had no eye or ear for aught but Griddlebone,
And the Lady seemed enraptured by his manly baritone,
Disposed to relaxation, and awaiting no surprise—
But the moonlight shone reflected from a thousand bright blue eyes.

And closer still and closer the sampans circled round,
And yet from all the enemy there was not heard a sound.
The lovers sang their last duet, in danger of their lives—
For the foe was armed with toasting forks and cruel carving knives.

Then GILBERT gave the signal to his fierce Mongolian horde;
With a frightful burst of fireworks the Chinks they swarmed aboard.
Abandoning their sampans, and their pullaways and junks,
They battened down the hatches on the crew within their bunks.

Then Griddlebone she gave a screech, for she was badly skeered;
I am sorry to admit it, but she quickly disappeared.
She probably escaped with ease, I'm sure she was not drowned—
But a serried ring of flashing steel Growltiger did surround.

The ruthless foe pressed forward, in stubborn rank on rank;
Growltiger to his vast surprise was forced to walk the plank.
He who a hundred victims had driven to that drop,
At the end of all his crimes was forced to go ker-flip, ker-flop.

Oh there was joy in Wapping when the news flew through the land;
At Maidenhead and Henley there was dancing on the strand.
Rats were roasted whole at Brentford, and at Victoria Dock,
And a day of celebration was commanded in Bangkok.

A Cat

Edward Thomas

She had a name among the children;
But no one loved though some one owned
Her, locked her out of doors at bedtime,
And had her kittens duly drowned.

Cat Accompanying Game, Jan Fyt (*Musée des Beaux-Arts, Nantes*)

In spring, nevertheless, this cat
Ate blackbirds, thrushes, nightingales,
And birds of bright voice, and plume, and flight,
As well as scraps from neighbours' pails.

I loathed and hated her for this;
One speckle on a thrush's breast
Was worth a million such; and yet
She lived long till God gave her rest.

Ming's Biggest Prey

Patricia Highsmith

Ming was resting comfortably on the foot of his mistress' bunk, when the man picked him up by the back of the neck, stuck him out on the deck and closed the cabin door. Ming's blue eyes widened in shock and brief anger, then nearly closed again because of the brilliant sunlight. It was not the first time Ming had been thrust out of the cabin rudely, and Ming realised that the man did it when his mistress, Elaine, was not looking.

The sailboat now offered no shelter from the sun, but Ming was not yet too warm. He leapt easily to the cabin roof and stepped onto the coil of rope just behind the mast. Ming liked the rope coil as a couch, because he could see everything from the height, the cup shape of the rope protected him from strong breezes, and also minimised the swaying and sudden changes of angle of the *White Lark*, since it was more or less the centre point. But just now the sail had been taken down, because Elaine and the man had eaten lunch, and often they had a siesta afterward, during which time, Ming knew, the man didn't like him in the cabin. Lunchtime was all right. In fact, Ming had just lunched on delicious grilled fish and a bit of lobster. Now, lying in a relaxed curve on the coil of rope, Ming opened his mouth in a great yawn, then with his slant eyes almost closed against the strong sunlight, gazed at the beige hills and the white and pink houses and hotels that circled the bay of Acapulco. Between the *White Lark* and the shore where people plashed inaudibly, the sun twinkled on the water's surface like thousands of tiny electric lights going on and off. A water-skier went by, skimming up white spray behind him. Such activity! Ming half dozed, feeling the heat of the sun sink into his fur. Ming was from New York, and he considered Acapulco a great improvement over his environment in the first weeks of his life. He remembered a sunless box with straw on the bottom, three or four other kittens in with him, and a window behind which giant forms paused for a few moments, tried to catch his attention by tapping, then passed on. He did not remember his mother at all. One day a young woman who smelled of something pleasant came into the place and took him away—away from the ugly, frightening smell of dogs, of medicine and parrot dung. Then they went on what Ming now knew was an aeroplane. He was quite used to aeroplanes now and rather liked them. On aeroplanes he sat on Elaine's lap, or slept on her lap, and there were always titbits to eat if he was hungry.

Elaine spent much of the day in a shop in Acapulco, where dresses and slacks and bathing suits hung on all the walls. This place smelled clean and fresh, there were flowers in pots and in boxes out front, and the floor was of cool blue and white tile. Ming had perfect freedom to wander out into the patio behind the shop, or to sleep in his basket in a corner. There was more sunlight in front of the shop, but mischievous boys often tried to grab him if he sat in front, and Ming could never relax there.

Ming liked best lying in the sun with his mistress on one of the long canvas chairs on their terrace at home. What Ming did not like were the people she sometimes invited to their house, people who spent the night, people by the score who stayed up very late eating and drinking, playing the gramophone or the piano—people who separated him from Elaine. People who

The Music Lesson, Jean-Honoré Fragonard (*Musée du Louvre, Paris*)

[178]

stepped on his toes, people who sometimes picked him up from behind before he could do anything about it, so that he had to squirm and fight to get free, people who stroked him roughly,
people who closed a door somewhere, locking him in. *People!* Ming detested people. In all the
the world, he liked only Elaine. Elaine loved him and understood him.

Especially this man called Teddie Ming detested now. Teddie was around all the time
lately. Ming did not like the way Teddie looked at him, when Elaine was not watching. And
sometimes Teddie, when Elaine was not near, muttered something which Ming knew was a
threat. Or a command to leave the room. Ming took it calmly. Dignity was to be preserved.
Besides, wasn't his mistress on his side? The man was the intruder. When Elaine was watching,
the man sometimes pretended a fondness for him, but Ming always moved gracefully but
unmistakably in another direction.

Ming's nap was interrupted by the sound of the cabin door opening. He heard Elaine and
the man laughing and talking. The big red-orange sun was near the horizon.

"Ming!" Elaine came over to him. "Aren't you getting *cooked*, darling? I thought you were
in!"

"So did I!" said Teddie.

Ming purred as he always did when he awakened. She picked him up gently, cradled him in
her arms, and took him below into the suddenly cool shade of the cabin. She was talking to the
man, and not in a gentle tone. She set Ming down in front of his dish of water, and though he
was not thirsty, he drank a little to please her. Ming did feel addled by the heat, and he staggered
a little.

Elaine took a wet towel and wiped Ming's face, his ears and his four paws. Then she laid
him gently on the bunk that smelled of Elaine's perfume but also of the man whom Ming
detested.

Now his mistress and the man were quarrelling, Ming could tell from the tone. Elaine was
staying with Ming, sitting on the edge of the bunk. Ming at last heard the splash that meant
Teddie had dived into the water. Ming hoped he stayed there, hoped he drowned, hoped he
never came back. Elaine wet a bathtowel in the aluminium sink, wrung it out, spread it on the
bunk, and lifted Ming onto it. She brought water, and now Ming was thirsty, and drank. She
left him to sleep again while she washed and put away the dishes. These were comfortable
sounds that Ming liked to hear.

But soon there was another *plash* and *plop*, Teddie's wet feet on the deck, and Ming was
awake again.

The tone of quarrelling recommenced. Elaine went up the few steps onto the deck. Ming,
tense but with his chin still resting on the moist bathtowel, kept his eyes on the cabin door. It
was Teddie's feet that he heard descending. Ming lifted his head slightly, aware that there was no
exit behind him, that he was trapped in the cabin. The man paused with a towel in his hands,
staring at Ming.

Ming relaxed completely, as he might do preparatory to a yawn, and this caused his eyes to
cross. Ming then let his tongue slide a little way out of his mouth. The man started to say something, looked as if he wanted to hurl the wadded towel at Ming, but he wavered, whatever he
had been going to say never got out of his mouth, and he threw the towel in the sink, then bent
to wash his face. It was not the first time Ming had let his tongue slide out at Teddie. Lots of
people laughed when Ming did this, if they were people at a party, for instance, and Ming
rather enjoyed that. But Ming sensed that Teddie took it as a hostile gesture of some kind,
which was why Ming did it deliberately to Teddie, whereas among other people, it was often
an accident when Ming's tongue slid out.

[179]

The Woman with Cat, Pierre Bonnard (*Kunsthalle Bremen*)

The quarrelling continued. Elaine made coffee. Ming began to feel better, and went on deck again, because the sun had now set. Elaine had started the motor, and they were gliding slowly toward the shore. Ming caught the song of birds, the odd screams like shrill phrases of certain birds that cried only at sunset. Ming looked forward to the adobe house on the cliff that was his and his mistress' home. He knew that the reason she did not leave him at home (where he would have been more comfortable) when she went on the boat, was because she was afraid that people might trap him, even kill him. Ming understood. People had tried to grab him from almost under Elaine's eyes. Once he had been all the way in a cloth bag suddenly, and though fighting as hard as he could, he was not sure he would have been able to get out, if Elaine had not hit the boy herself and grabbed the bag from him.

Ming had intended to jump up on the cabin roof again, but after glancing at it, he decided to save his strength, so he crouched on the warm, gently sloping deck with his feet tucked in, and gazed at the approaching shore. Now he could hear guitar music from the beach. The voices of his mistress and the man had come to a halt. For a few moments, the loudest sound was the chug-chug-chug of the boat's motor. Then Ming heard the man's bare feet climbing the cabin steps. Ming did not turn his head to look at him, but his ears twitched back a little, involuntarily. Ming looked at the water just the distance of a short leap in front of him and below him. Strangely, there was no sound from the man behind him. The hair on Ming's neck prickled, and Ming glanced over his right shoulder.

At that instant, the man bent forward and rushed at Ming with his arms outspread.

Ming was on his feet at once, darting straight toward the man which was the only direction of safety on the railless deck, and the man swung his left arm and cuffed Ming in the chest. Ming went flying backward, claws scraping the deck, but his hind legs went over the edge. Ming clung with his front feet to the sleek wood which gave him little hold, while his hind legs worked to heave him up, worked at the side of the boat which sloped to Ming's disadvantage.

The man advanced to shove a foot against Ming's paws, but Elaine came up the cabin steps just then.

"What's happening? *Ming!*"

Ming's strong hind legs were getting him onto the deck little by little. The man had knelt as if to lend a hand. Elaine had fallen onto her knees, also, and had Ming by the back of the neck now.

Ming relaxed, hunched on the deck. His tail was wet.

"He fell overboard!" Teddie said. "It's true he's groggy. Just lurched over and fell when the boat gave a dip."

"It's the sun. Poor *Ming!*" Elaine held the cat .

The man came down into the cabin. Elaine had Ming on the bunk and was talking softly to him. Ming's heart was still beating fast. He was alert against the man at the wheel, even though Elaine was with him. Ming was aware that they had entered the little cove where they always went before getting off the boat.

Here were the friends and allies of Teddie, whom Ming detested by association, although these were merely Mexican boys. Two or three boys in shorts called "Señor Teddie!" and offered a hand to Elaine to climb onto the dock, took the rope attached to the front of the boat, offered to carry "Ming!–Ming!" Ming leapt onto the dock himself and crouched, waiting for Elaine, ready to dart away from any other hand that might reach for him. And there were several brown hands making a rush for him, so that Ming had to keep jumping aside. There were laughs, yelps, stomps of bare feet on wooden boards. But there was also the reassuring voice of Elaine, warning them off. Ming knew she was busy carrying off the plastic satchels, locking the cabin

[181]

door. Teddie with the aid of one of the Mexican boys was stretching the canvas over the cabin now. And Elaine's sandalled feet were beside Ming. Ming followed her as she walked away. A boy took the things Elaine was carrying, then she picked Ming up.

They got into the big car without a roof that belonged to Teddie, and drove up the winding road toward Elaine's and Ming's house. One of the boys was driving. Now the tone in which Elaine and Teddie were speaking was calmer, softer. The man laughed. Ming sat tensely on his mistress' lap. He could feel her concern for him in the way she stroked him and touched the back of his neck. The man reached out to put his fingers on Ming's back, and Ming gave a low growl that rose and fell and rumbled deep in his throat.

"Well, well," said the man, pretending to be amused and took his hand away.

Elaine's voice had stopped in the middle of something she was saying. Ming was tired, and wanted nothing more than to take a nap on the big bed at home. The bed was covered with a red and white striped blanket of thin wool.

Hardly had Ming thought of this, when he found himself in the cool, fragrant atmosphere of his own home, being lowered gently onto the bed with the soft woollen cover. His mistress kissed his cheek, and said something with the word hungry in it. Ming understood, at any rate. He was to tell her when he was hungry.

Ming dozed, and awakened at the sound of voices on the terrace a couple of yards away, past the open glass doors. Now it was dark. Ming could see one end of the table, and could tell from the quality of the light that there were candles on the table. Concha, the servant who slept in the house, was clearing the table. Ming heard her voice, then the voices of Elaine and the man. Ming smelled cigar smoke. Ming jumped to the floor and sat for a moment looking out the door toward the terrace. He yawned, then arched his back and stretched, and limbered up his muscles by digging his claws into the thick straw carpet. Then he slipped out to the right on the terrace and glided silently down the long stairway of broad stones to the garden below. The garden was like a jungle or a forest. Avocado trees and mango trees grew as high as the terrace itself, there were bougainvilleas against the wall, orchids in the trees, and magnolias and several camellias which Elaine had planted. Ming could hear birds twittering and stirring in their nests. Sometimes he climbed trees to get at their nests, but tonight he was not in the mood, though he was no longer tired. The voices of his mistress and the man disturbed him. His mistress was not a friend of the man's tonight, that was plain.

Concha was probably still in the kitchen, and Ming decided to go in and ask her for something to eat. Concha liked him. One maid who had not liked him had been dismissed by Elaine. Ming thought he fancied barbecued pork. That was what his mistress and the man had eaten tonight. The breeze blew fresh from the ocean, ruffling Ming's fur slightly. Ming felt completely recovered from the awful experience of nearly falling into the sea.

Now the terrace was empty of people. Ming went left, back into the bedroom, and was at once aware of the man's presence, though there was no light on and Ming could not see him. The man was standing by the dressing-table, opening a box. Again involuntarily Ming gave a low growl which rose and fell, and Ming remained frozen in the position he had been in when he first became aware of the man, his right front paw extended for the next step. Now his ears were back, he was prepared to spring in any direction, although the man had not seen him.

"Ssss-st! Damn you!" the man said in a whisper. He stamped his foot, not very hard, to make the cat go away.

Ming did not move at all. Ming heard the soft rattle of the white necklace which belonged to his mistress. The man put it into his pocket, then moved to Ming's right, out the door that went into the big living-room. Ming now heard the clink of a bottle against glass, heard liquid

Red Tabby, Sheila Robinson (*Artist's Collection*)

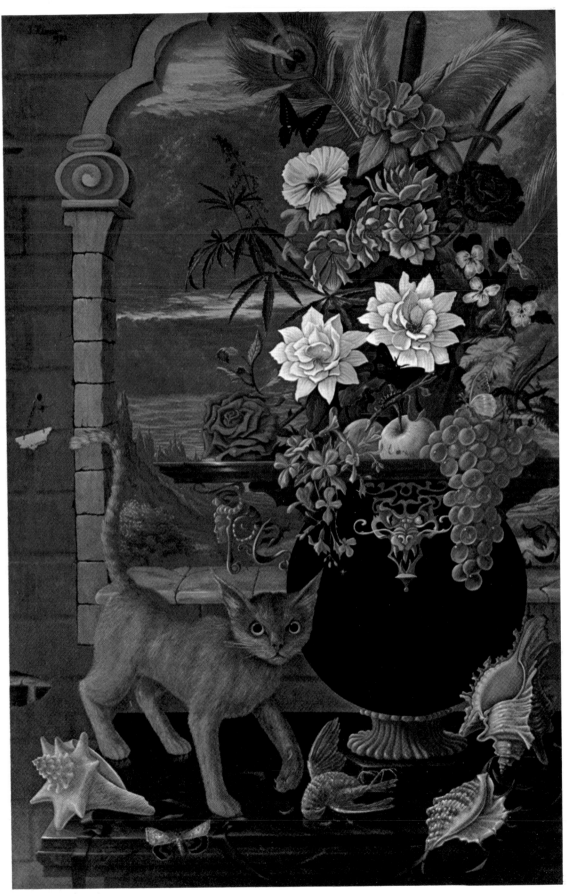

Flowercat, Johan Hermsen (© *Verkerke Reprodukties BV*)

being poured. Ming went through the same door and turned left toward the kitchen.

Here he miaowed, and was greeted by Elaine and Concha. Concha had her radio turned on to music.

"Fish?—Pork. He likes pork," Elaine said, speaking the odd form of words which she used with Concha.

Ming, without much difficulty, conveyed his preference for pork, and got it. He fell to with a good appetite. Concha was exclaiming "Ah-eee-ee!" as his mistress spoke with her, spoke at length. Then Concha bent to stroke him, and Ming put up with it, still looking down at his plate, until she left off and he could finish his meal. Then Elaine left the kitchen. Concha gave him some of the tinned milk, which he loved, in his now empty saucer, and Ming lapped this up. Then he rubbed himself against her bare leg by way of thanks, and went out of the kitchen, made his way cautiously into the living-room en route to the bedroom. But now his mistress and the man were out on the terrace. Ming had just entered the bedroom, when he heard Elaine call:

"Ming? Where are you?"

Ming went to the terrace door and stopped, and sat on the threshold.

Elaine was sitting sideways at the end of the table, and the candlelight was bright on her long fair hair, on the white of her trousers. She slapped her thigh, and Ming jumped onto her lap.

There is always Another, Marcus Stone (*Tate Gallery, London*)

The man said something in a low tone, something not nice.

Elaine replied something in the same tone. But she laughed a little.

Then the telephone rang.

Elaine put Ming down, and went into the living-room toward the telephone.

The man finished what was in his glass, muttered something at Ming, then set the glass on the table. He got up and tried to circle Ming, or to get him toward the edge of the terrace, Ming realised, and Ming also realised that the man was drunk—therefore moving slowly and a little clumsily. The terrace had a parapet about as high as the man's hips, but it was broken by grilles in three places, grilles with bars wide enough for Ming to pass through, though Ming never did, merely looked through the grilles sometimes. It was plain to Ming that the man wanted to drive him through one of the grilles, or grab him and toss him over the terrace parapet. There was nothing easier for Ming than to elude him. Then the man picked up a chair and swung it suddenly, catching Ming on the hip. That had been quick, and it hurt. Ming took the nearest exit, which was down the outside steps that led to the garden.

The man started down the steps after him. Without reflecting, Ming dashed back up the few steps he had come, keeping close to the wall which was in shadow. The man hadn't seen him, Ming knew. Ming leapt to the terrace parapet, sat down and licked a paw once to recover and collect himself. His heart beat fast as if he were in the middle of a fight. And hatred ran in his veins. Hatred burned his eyes as he crouched and listened to the man uncertainly climbing the steps below him. The man came into view.

Ming tensed himself for a jump, then jumped as hard as he could, landing with all four feet on the man's right arm near the shoulder. Ming clung to the cloth of the man's white jacket, but they were both falling. The man groaned. Ming hung on. Branches crackled. Ming could not tell up from down. Ming jumped off the man, became aware of direction and of the earth too late and landed on his side. Almost at the same time, he heard the thud of the man hitting the ground, then of his body rolling a little way, then there was silence. Ming had to breathe fast with his mouth open until his chest stopped hurting. From the direction of the man, he could smell drink, cigar, and the sharp odour that meant fear. But the man was not moving.

Ming could now see quite well. There was even a bit of moonlight. Ming headed for the steps again, had to go a long way through the bush, over stones and sand, to where the steps began. Then he glided up and arrived once more upon the terrace.

Elaine was just coming onto the terrace.

"Teddie?" she called. Then she went back into the bedroom where she turned on a lamp. She went into the kitchen. Ming followed her. Concha had left the light on, but Concha was now in her own room, where the radio played.

Elaine opened the front door.

The man's car was still in the driveway, Ming saw. Now Ming's hip had begun to hurt, or now he had begun to notice it. It caused him to limp a little. Elaine noticed this, touched his back, and asked him what was the matter. Ming only purred.

"Teddie?—Where are you?" Elaine called.

She took a torch and shone it down into the garden, down among the great trunks of the avocado trees, among the orchids and the lavender and pink blossoms of the bougainvilleas. Ming, safe beside her on the terrace parapet, followed the beam of the torch with his eyes and purred with content. The man was not below here, but below and to the right. Elaine went to the terrace steps and carefully, because there was no rail here, only broad steps, pointed the beam of the light downward. Ming did not bother looking. He sat on the terrace where the steps began.

"Teddie!" she said. "*Teddie!*" Then she ran down the steps.

Ming still did not follow her. He heard her draw in her breath. Then she cried:

"*Concha!*"

Elaine ran back up the steps.

Concha had come out of her room. Elaine spoke to Concha. Then Concha became excited. Elaine went to the telephone, and spoke for a short while, then she and Concha went down the steps together. Ming settled himself with his paws tucked under him on the terrace, which was still faintly warm from the day's sun. A car arrived. Elaine came up the steps, and went and opened the front door. Ming kept out of the way on the terrace, in a shadowy corner, as three or

Woman with Leaping Cat, Robert Colquhoun (*Tate Gallery, London*)

[185]

four strange men came out on the terrace and tramped down the steps. There was a great deal of talk below, noises of feet, breaking of bushes, and then the smell of all of them mounted the steps, the smell of tobacco, sweat, and the familiar smell of blood. The man's blood. Ming was pleased, as he was pleased when he killed a bird and created this smell of blood under his own teeth. This was big prey. Ming, unnoticed by any of the others, stood up to his full height as the group passed with the corpse, and inhaled the aroma of his victory with a lifted nose.

Then suddenly the house was empty. Everyone had gone, even Concha. Ming drank a little water from his bowl in the kitchen, then went to his mistress' bed, curled against the slope of the pillows, and fell fast asleep. He was awakened by the rr-rr-r of an unfamiliar car. Then the front door opened, and he recognised the step of Elaine and then Concha. Ming stayed where he was. Elaine and Concha talked softly for a few minutes. Then Elaine came into the bedroom. The lamp was still on. Ming watched her slowly open the box on her dressing table, and into it she let fall the white necklace that made a little clatter. Then she closed the box. She began to unbutton her shirt, but before she had finished, she flung herself on the bed and stroked Ming's head, lifted his left paw and pressed it gently so that the claws came forth.

"Oh Ming—Ming," she said.

Ming recognised the tones of love.

The Colubriad

William Cowper

Close by the threshold of a door nail'd fast
Three kittens sat: each kitten look'd aghast.
I, passing swift and inattentive by,
At the three kittens cast a careless eye;
Not much concern'd to know what they did there,
Not deeming kittens worth a poet's care.
But presently a loud and furious hiss
Caused me to stop, and to exclaim—what's this?
When, lo! upon the threshold met my view,
With head erect, and eyes of fiery hue,
A viper, long as Count de Grasse's queue.
Forth from his head his forkèd tongue he throws,
Darting it full against a kitten's nose;
Who having never seen in field or house
The like, sat still and silent, as a mouse:
Only, projecting with attention due
Her whisker'd face, she ask'd him—who are you?

On to the hall went I, with pace not slow,
But swift as lightning, for a long Dutch hoe;
With which well arm'd I hasten'd to the spot,
To find the viper. But I found him not,
And, turning up the leaves and shrubs around,
Found only, that he was not to be found.
But still the kittens, sitting as before
Sat watching close the bottom of the door.
I hope—said I—the villain I would kill
Has slipt between the door and the door's sill;
And if I make dispatch, and follow hard,
No doubt but I shall find him in the yard—
For long ere now it should have been rehears'd,
'Twas in the garden that I found him first.
E'en there I found him; there the full-grown cat
His head with velvet paw did gently pat,
As curious as the kittens erst had been
To learn what this phenomenon might mean.
Fill'd with heroic ardour at the sight,
And fearing every moment he might bite,
And rob our household of our only cat
That was of age to combat with a rat,
With outstretch'd hoe I slew him at the door,
And taught him NEVER TO COME THERE NO MORE.

Aunty and Her Cats

Paul Ableman

Sometimes my great-aunt would be sitting at her dressing-table, in the curve of the big bow window, brushing her white, fine, still abundant hair with a matched set of engraved silver hair-brushes, the gift of a Viennese count perhaps—or a German baron. More probably, at that time of day, she would be seated on the low sofa in front of the blazing gas-fire, legs apart to reveal the ends of long, silk bloomers, spectacles perched on her dainty nose, round, astonishingly-smooth face wrinkled into a frown of dismay as she studied the *Evening Standard*.

"Ach! Terrible it is—terrible!"

"What is?"

"Have you not heard? This earthquake in—Brazil, is it?"

She would peer forwards at the elusive print and then amend, "Ah—Mehico—Mehico!

Twelve people killed and three buried alive! This is—such a tragedy! These poor people! Terrible!"

In my callow intolerance, I felt merely irritated by her distress. In the midst of a desperate war that had, amongst greater enormities, deprived her of everything she owned, Aunty would fuss endlessly about some trivial natural disaster. But the thing that, shamefully, annoyed me most about her was her devotion to Nicki and Simon, her two sluggish, overfed cats. These were regularly the recipient of tidbits which in wartime, should clearly have been reserved for human beings. It infuriated me to see Aunty slip morsels of precious meat into the cats' mouths or even pour them a saucer of priceless cream. I sensed that Aunty loved those cats more than any other living things and this seemed to me monstrous when my aunt Olga had, with incredible pains, snatched her from Nazi Germany and installed her in the greatest luxury our guest-house could offer. There was no prospect of any material return since all Aunty's possessions in Bavaria had been seized. The old lady, who had been the mistress of many aristocrats, was now a pauper.

I was angered then by Aunty's pampering of her cats but perhaps even more so by her intermittent bursts of fury with them. Through the thin ceiling, if I happened to be in Olga's basement room, I might suddenly hear a hubbub from Aunty's room above:

"Pfa! Pfooi! Villain! Verdamt! Aus! Aus! Geh—Schwein!"

We would also hear dismal thudding and scratching sounds. Olga would leap to her feet, exclaiming, "Oh my God—not again!"

And hasten out of the room and up the stairs. I would listen sardonically to Aunty's voice, shrill with denunciation, and Olga's soothing one. I knew, from abundant precedent, exactly what had happened. Nicki or Simon, shaking off its overfed torpor and responding to atavistic impulse, would once again have caught a bird and, blissfully and idiotically forgetful of its reception after the last such escapade, would have carried the bedraggled corpse up the garden steps, along the balcony ledge, through the noble French windows and finally deposited it proudly at Aunty's feet. The old lady would then have risen like one of the Furies, stamped her foot at the disconcerted animal and abused it in ringing terms. She could never bring herself actually to assault her darlings but sometimes she went so far as to pursue fat, tortoiseshell Simon or black, bulging Nicki with a broom and many a menacing feint. And, sometimes for days on end, she would be inconsolable. When Olga attempted to defend the obese predator, extolling some imaginary feline virtue, Aunty would angrily contradict her:

"No! Nicki is a swine! I have told him before—he must not kill the birds! Ach, the pig! I never will see him again!"

Sadly, tenderly, she would take up the little huddle of feathers and stump off with it across the room, down the steps to the garden and there, right at the end under the plane tree, bury it with a trowel, pausing repeatedly to make a fierce gesture towards a black nose and a pair of glowing, carnivore's eyes that peered apprehensively out at her from the jungle of a peony bush.

I found these episodes baffling and excessively irritating. Once or twice, I tried to remonstrate with Aunty, "After all, it's part of their nature."

"Ja, ja." She would nod sadly.

"I mean it's instinct. Cats are hunting animals."

"He is a swine, that Nicki!"

"But, Aunty, it's utterly illogical. It's like—like setting something on fire and then being upset because it burns."

"He will not get any cream on Sunday. I will punish him."

"But that's crazy."

"Ach, the poor little bird! The little bird!"

Cat with Cock

And I would note, with uncomfortable surprise, that Aunty's large, grey-blue eyes, a little discoloured with age, were full of tears. She had no imagination, no philosophical or scientific view of the universe, but—rivalling feats attributed to deity—she noted and mourned the fall of a sparrow.

The Rat-Catcher and Cats

John Gay

The rats by night such mischief did,
Betty was every morning chid.
They undermined whole sides of bacon,
Her cheese was sapp'd, her tarts were taken.
Her pasties fenced with thickest paste,
Were all demolish'd, and laid waste.
She cursed the Cat for want of duty,
Who left her foes a constant booty.

An engineer, of noted skill,
Engaged to stop the growing ill.

From room to room he now surveys
Their haunts, their works, their secret ways;
Finds where they 'scape and ambuscade,
And whence the nightly sally's made,

And envious Cat, from place to place,
Unseen attends his silent pace.
She saw that if his trade went on,
The purring race must be undone;
So, secretly removes his baits,
And ev'ry stratagem defeats.

Again he sets the poison'd toils,
And Puss again the labour foils.

What foe (to frustrate my designs)
My schemes thus nightly countermines?
Incensed, he cries, this very hour
The wretch shall bleed beneath my power.

So said, a pond'rous trap he brought,
And in the fact poor Puss was caught.

Smuggler, says he, thou shalt be made
A victim to our loss of trade.

The captive Cat, with piteous mews,
For pardon, life, and freedom sues.
A sister of the science spare;

The Ratcatcher, Thomas Woodward (*Tate Gallery, London*)

One int'rest is our common care.
　　What insolence! the man replied;
Shall cats with us the game divide?
Were all your interloping band
Extinguish'd or expell'd the land,
We Rat-catchers might raise our fees,
Sole guardians of a nation's cheese!
　　A Cat, who saw the lifted knife,
Thus spoke, and saved her sister's life:
　　In ev'ry age and clime we see,
Two of a trade can ne'er agree.
Each hates his neighbour for encroaching;
'Squire stigmatises 'squire for poaching;
Beauties with beauties are in arms,
And scandal pelts each other's charms;
Kings, too, their neighbour kings dethrone,
In hope to make the world their own,
But let us limit out desires,
Not war like beauties, kings, and 'squires!
For though we both one prey pursue,
There's game enough for us and you.

[191]

Cat and Fiddle

Roy Fuller

Dinner at the Club: always a blend of boredom and, à la Henry James, stimulation at hearing of the lives of others. When Bobby Freeman sat next to me at the round table the mix seemed likely to have gone wrong for the evening. He talked, as he often does, about crime, fictional and real, even recounting a few plots. He is one of those who talk so much that food accompanies their words, sometimes flecking one's clothes. He made the ancient point that we can never know about the "perfect" crime precisely because of its perfection. Still, there were a few murders which might be classed as perfect simply by reason of the meagre number of people who suspected them of being murders. Who, for example, except himself, was aware of the Guild case?

"Sir Hugh's?" I asked jokingly, really envisaging something involving a political or craft organisation of the slightly eccentric kind, which Bobby might well have special information about. We both knew Hugh Guild, Bobby better than I.

"Yes."

Even as I laughed an uneasy memory came of the deaths in Hugh's life. "Oh, really, Bobby."

"This is what I had from Hugh himself," said Bobby. "As a novelist you'll be interested."

When Hugh retired from the Museum, he and his wife went to live in some village on the far side of Newbury. (I put down what Bobby told me, embellished with my own knowledge.) The house was called "The Cottages": someone had converted three cottages into the one dwelling. Hugh bought an adjoining paddock with an eye to enlarging the garden. He had enough money to do so and to titivate the place further, having sold the Chelsea house he'd owned all the time he'd directed the Museum.

Odd to contemplate Hugh Guild in the country. He had been a dogged world traveller on Museum business: when at home, an equally dogged party-goer and diner-out. I remember the first time I saw him at an evening-dress function being amazed at the splendour of his decorations—which included a fair selection of foreign orders—and thinking that perhaps a strong motive for such appearances was the opportunity to display the evidence of his honours. At cocktail parties his shiny black hair (which never changed colour, even in his sixties) could be seen surrounded by the more desiccated and abundant hair of the young—his books, and exhibitions at the Museum, which always seemed just to anticipate new enthusiasms and shifts in taste, ensured him an audience of that constitution.

Not that he appeared to do more than accept their homage. In England at any rate he was always accompanied by Lady Guild, growing more and more to seem mother rather than wife. Though she, too, had kept thin, a somewhat battered mask was quite early presented: one eyelid was inclined to droop; the chin sported a sprouting mole. The figure, by no means straight-backed, was surmounted by white hair in a very old-fashioned "bob". The total effect was inclined to the witchlike.

Helen Guild's transmogrification into a countrywoman was also surprising, since she too had been active in urban affairs, mainly of an obscure "good works" kind. The fact was that at sixty-five they were both rather weary and possessed ailments not less lowering for being scarcely definable. Hugh found himself relieved to give up the responsibilities of administration. Their notion of regular London "days" was not fulfilled. They dropped almost completely out of their former worlds.

Yet Hugh didn't feel that his life was on a finally downward slope. Rather he saw himself as re-charging his batteries for a "final period" of somewhat changed scope—the authorship of different kinds of books and articles, possibily some new appointment in the public service sphere. The decorations had not been permanently mothballed, as it were: they would eventually re-emerge, perhaps with a couple of distinguished additions.

Nevertheless, the Guilds at first were quiet and shaky. Hugh's insomnia wasn't mathematically more severe than in London but since he hadn't to be on parade the following day he positively indulged his nocturnal wakefulness—going downstairs to read for long periods, making himself drinks and snacks, even strolling in the enlarging garden.

"We've got mice," he told his wife at breakfast one day.

"Have we?"

"I saw one when I came down to make my Ovaltine last night."

"We had mice at Bramerton Street," said Lady Guild.

"I never saw any."

"Well, in those days you didn't make a habit of visiting the kitchen in the middle of the night."

Quite soon, Hugh raised the question again.

"Those bloody mice come out and sit up and watch me."

"I expect they're only field mice," said Lady Guild.

"I don't care what they are, I don't like them. I find I've an unreasoning fear of them. I'm quite uneasy when I have to go into the kitchen and switch on the light."

"You should try harder to get to sleep again upstairs."

"I think we ought to buy a cat."

"We've never had pets," said Lady Guild. "We don't know how to deal with them."

"A cat wouldn't need 'dealing with'."

"Um."

The pub on the village green had been raised in status by the brewers—with a licensee to match, possessing a military title. The Guilds had begun by patronising the bar luncheon and then Hugh took to dropping in at the end of an evening stroll. To the landlord he told his mice story. Also behind the bar was a Mrs Farrer, a pale young woman, usually with a cigarette sticking out of her mouth. She said that the pub's charwoman's cat, nondescript itself, had had kittens, the father reputed to be a Persian of prize breed. They were going gratis.

"Which kind do you want?" Mrs Farrer asked Hugh. "Boy or girl?"

Had he been entirely serious about acquiring a cat? Under Mrs Farrer's laconic but penetrating interrogation he felt suddenly carried along by events.

"Girl," he said, matching her off-handedness, but with a sense of some unusual step taken, not wholly displeasing.

Lady Guild disclaimed any responsibility for the slight new complication in their lives. Though not actively hostile, she was uncharmed by the mainly black, diminutive animal that after a few hours of cowering and peeing under furniture scuttled across the floors, climbed curtains and attacked feet.

"That kitten is very bold," Hugh observed with satisfaction. "The mice had better look out."

Temptation, Gabriel Gresly (*Musée du Dijon*)

He began to refer to the creature as "Boldero". When Lady Guild asked him if that was to be its name and he affirmed it, she remarked it was an odd one.

" 'Boldero' was a *nom de plume* assumed by the poet Grigson in the Thirties," he said.

"Grigson?"

"You remember him. Friend of Bill Coldstream."

In a few days' time Lady Guild heard her husband shouting "Martin, Martin" in the garden. When challenged, he said he'd been calling the kitten.

"I thought it was called Boldero," said Lady Guild.

"The *nom de plume* was 'Martin Boldero'. I've shortened it to Martin."

"But the animal is female."

"That's true," Hugh had to admit.

"Besides, it has fleas."

Though Hugh would have been on safer ground in attacking this final statement merely as a *non sequitur*, he disputed the actual infestation. "The *Cat and Fiddle* cleaner is a very well turned out person and I'm sure her house is the same."

It was an indication of Hugh's ignorance of "pets" that he seemed to confuse human and feline parasites. Stroking Boldero (or Martin) the very day of this conversation, he saw an insect on the back of his thumb which, instead of flying or crawling away in a ordinary manner, disappeared with a disreputable leap. Far more for Boldero's comfort than in the interests of domestic hygiene, Hugh took action without delay, plunging the animal in a wash-basinful of tepid water, tinctured with shampoo and Dettol. Its struggles were fairly effectively mastered but the immediate result was appalling. In his hands shivered a skeletal kitten, all the more horrifying for the thin layer of fur plastered to the bone. The apparition jerked out of the towel Hugh had ready, and disappeared downstairs under a chiffonier which Hugh laboriously moved, fearing that Boldero would catch a chill, even pneumonia. The kitten, cornered, flew out of the window, breaking a nice little saucer in the process.

In the evening, when the parties were reconciled, Hugh saw a flea slither from a patch of Boldero's preternaturally-shining white to the ampler cover of the black. He removed the kitten from his knee to the floor, but without haste, since Lady Guild was in the room and she had already commented adversely on the breakage and other depredations of the afternoon bathe. "I'm afraid that flea-ridden beast will have to go," she had concluded unemotionally.

Hugh was agreeably surprised to see that Boots in Newbury devoted considerable shelf space to feline remedies and cosmetics: it was like finding a cache of books of one's special interest in an unpromising secondhand shop. He came away with several items, including anti-flea powder, which as soon as Lady Guild was out of the way for half an hour he used according to the directions.

The parasites went on being apparent. The mice have been extirpated only to be replaced by fleas, he thought, emitting a wry snigger. He would have passed on the jest to his wife had he not feared her irony: moreover, he was still carrying on his fleaing in secrecy. This eventually had to be done in his dressing-room, for the final and most effective mode involved a comb and a bowl of water, the latter hard to conceal at short notice. The fleas emerged dazed on the comb or, with even greater chance of capture, trapped in its teeth. They were drowned in the bowl of water; in later sessions more humanely cracked between Hugh's thumb-nails, the betraying water dispensed with.

The resultant blood or guts—or, indeed, any part of the operation—did not disgust him. The small black specks, discernible against the white parts of the fur, which he had thought to be flea eggs, left a trail of red in the water: obviously they were flea excrement, composed of Boldero's gore. The discovery held the impersonality and pleasure of scientific knowledge. Nevertheless, the whole process undoubtedly brought on a rapid intimacy and sympathy, as between patient and nurse.

"How are you getting on with that kitten?" Mrs Farrer asked Hugh when he had dropped into the *Cat and Fiddle* soon after these pulicine sessions. She had proved to be the landlady's daughter by a former marriage, now living, presumably more or less permanently, at the pub.

"Had great flea trouble," said Hugh, only too pleased to find a neutral ear in which to spill a prolix account of his therapy.

When he got home he saw that his wife had a long sticking plaster on the back of her hand. "What have you been doing to yourself?"

"Boldero scratched me."

"What were you doing to her?"

"Absolutely nothing."

"Are you sure?"

"Of course I'm sure," said Lady Guild.

"I mean are you sure you didn't do it pruning that rambler?"

"You must allow me to know whether or not I've been scratched by a cat."

"It's utterly out of character. Even when I tease her she knows exactly how far to go with her teeth and claws." He visualised raising his fist, Boldero clinging to it like the fur trimming of a sleeve. His mind was full of the touching flea saga, just related to Mrs Farrer. Also, the few drinks he'd had on an empty stomach encouraged his challenge of events which really it seemed unlikely his wife would be misconceived or mendacious about. Lady Guild, indeed, gave him a pitying look and went out of the room.

Simpkin at the Tailor's Bedside, Beatrix Potter (*Tate Gallery, London*)

"I'm sick of that cat," she was heard to say before she died, though the words were not distinct and Hugh's view was that she was still delirious and actually referring to a hat—the only one she possessed and which in their more public days she had to put on her bobbed locks when attending a garden party at Buck House and the like. It was an object of which she had made previous criticism. Rose-thorn or Boldero—medical opinion was neutral. The only certainty was that the septicaemia spreading from the scratched hand seemed unusually resistant. In a way, Hugh was thus supported in his persistence in his darling's defence.

Besides, to have admitted the cat's guilt would surely have lessened the comfort she afforded him in the early days of his widowerhood. It would have been tantamount to forgiving the the crime in the most heinous possible manner—cohabiting happily with the criminal. The weeks following the funeral marked Boldero's transition from foolish kittendom to vigorous young queenliness. Perhaps in the end the charm and condescending companionship were slightly overdone: Hugh began to feel himself the inferior partner in an alliance of the human and animal worlds.

"I'm glad we're seeing you here once more," said Mrs Farrer to Hugh in the saloon bar of the *Cat and Fiddle*. "If you don't mind my saying so, we thought you'd cut yourself off completely from the village. That would have been a pity."

Attaching himself to humanity again (if that was how the process was to be described), Hugh solved the faint mystery of Mrs Farrer's presence—or, rather, Mr Farrer's absence. During Lady Guild's illness Mrs Farrer's divorce had been finalised. For the time being she intended to stay on at the *Cat and Fiddle*, helping out her mother and the Captain. The status of her presence had changed from a lucky accident to a more or less permanent bonus the place might have superficially seemed ill-equipped to confer.

Returning home from his evening drink at what more and more inclined to be a latish hour, Hugh was always struck with Boldero's beauty. The face was blunt (stemming from her Persian ancestry) but the mongrel strain had prevented any exaggeration of the quality. The white on the face avoided eyes and nose so that—coral nostrils, peeled yellow-grape eyes supported by the glossiest black—she seemed permanently masked and enigmatic. The legs were short (feline mark of beauty, in contrast to the human), the feet substantial. It was a critical evening when this aesthetic sight prompted Hugh to think: Mrs Farrer is pretty, too.

His anticipation of ancient but not forgotten sensual enjoyment was fulfilled in the early days of his marriage with Mrs Farrer. It was months, perhaps a year or so, before he could think that *her* motive might have been to get away from the *Cat and Fiddle* and to be called Lady Guild. He disliked the appearance of male figures from her past life, even though she returned to sleep under his roof. And what came home to one in the second half of one's sixties was the rapidity and irreversibleness of emotional change. After all, he thought, sitting at his desk surrounded by the notebooks and card indices of his unfinished life's work, art is both the only sensible and the only enduring thing. Boldero's tail (she also was on the desk) waved slowly across the photograph of an Armenian stele. He seized the cursive object: the head came round, the little double keyhole of the nose astonishingly cold and wet—almost equally as astonishing as the phenomena his new marriage had reintroduced him to.

Very early one morning he found the second Lady Guild at the foot of the staircase, in a bad way. The conversion of the original three cottages involved, in the conception of the then owner, two staircases, one at either end of the resultant house. It was the minor staircase down which Lady Guild had tumbled. This was merely the original staircase of one of the constituent cottages, with its excessive proportion of riser to tread, and undeviating precipitousness from one floor to the other. Possibly the converter had envisaged a servant's end, a servant young and agile enough to move freely up and down what was scarcely more than a ladder.

"I fell over a cat," moaned Lady Guild, as Hugh held her hand, waiting for the ambulance.

"How could that be?"

"A strange cat must have got in."

"Strange", naturally, since Boldero could hardly be conceived as lurking in that uncomfortable area. Or was the *ci-devant* Mrs Farrer seeking to excuse Boldero, so beloved of Hugh, because she herself was guilty? It occurred too late to Hugh to ask her what she was doing at that hour using the staircase so remote from their bedrooms, because she lost consciousness in the ambulance and never recovered it. The haemorrhage spread rapidly through the brain.

I noticed (said Bobby) that Hugh didn't attempt in this case to interpret the crucial remark made as "Fell over a hat". Too outré to think Helen's envious shade had planted there the famous royal headgear. Nor would Bobby hear anything of my own suggestion that there *had* been an intruding cat—a tom after Boldero. He explained that Boldero had been spayed, adding that it was a pity the second Lady Guild hadn't been, too—all things considered.

The swift double loss might have put Hugh off The Cottages. But in fact he went on living there. Yet the image wasn't quite that of a bereaved old man consoled only by his cat. He began to be seen in London again, even (particularly when "decorations" were specified) at night. Somehow his batteries had been re-charged; or perhaps he had learned better how to draw on their remaining resources.

"Are you suggesting," I asked Bobby, "that that animal—Martin or whatever its name was —was the perfect murderer? Fiction has long ceased to deal with such whimsicalities." However, one has to admit that mysteries are often inclined to arise where cats are concerned, though more usually in such realms as unexplained absences or missing delicacies.

"You wouldn't acknowledge that a jealous cat—or a zealous cat—might direct a campaign against those it conceived to be damaging its master?"

"No."

"Nor would I."

"You wouldn't?"

"No," said Bobby.

"What on earth have we been talking about then?"

"I put it delicately to Hugh that in the eyes of some imaginative policeman *he* could have been the culprit. I called on him with the point in mind."

"Good Lord!"

"You see some possible lines of investigation," Bobby said. "Hugh collects Helen's penicillin prescription, or whatever it was, from the doctor and substitutes aspirin. Knowing the former Mrs Farrer has been using the far stairs for her illicit purposes, he stretches a wire across the top of them."

"What did he say?"

"What could he say? Only emphasise the accidental nature of the events."

"Did you see the less likely suspect?"

"Not on view. Not even a lingering grin. Though probably she was aware of my visit. When I drove away there was a bird in the car."

"What?" One momentarily conceived a female hitchhiker trading on her youth by actually seating herself in the parked vehicle.

"My Peugeot has a sun-roof. It had been open. A young starling had dropped—or been deposited—in the aperture. Awkward blind turn at the end of Hugh's lane. What with the squawking and fluttering I nearly failed to see a Post Office van. Eventually I stopped and let down the windows and managed to shoo the bird out. It didn't seem injured. Whether it was old enough to fly was doubtful. I didn't spend too much time worrying about it because when I got on the A4 I found the mice."

"In the car you mean?" One positively drained one's cognac. "You're having me on."

Drawing, Chas. Addams (© *1975 The New Yorker Magazine Inc*)

"Put in—or making their own way—through the sun-roof, as with the starling. Doubtless relatives of the mice that started the whole affair off. I don't share Hugh's unreasoning fear of mice but I must say it was awkward dealing with the beasts among the traffic. However, I survived, as is obvious."

"You knew too much. They wanted to get rid of you." Unusually with Bobby, one was carried away by his narrative.

"You mean Hugh and Boldero were actually working in concert?"

"Well, then, *she* wanted to get rid of you."

"I think the pronoun required is masculine," said Bobby.

The Black Cat

Edgar Allan Poe

For the most wild, yet most homely, narrative which I am about to pen, I neither expect nor solicit belief. Mad indeed would I be to expect it, in a case where my very senses reject their own evidence. Yet, mad am I not—and very surely do I not dream. But tomorrow I die, and today I would unburthen my soul. My immediate purpose is to place before the world, plainly, succinctly, and without comment, a series of mere household events. In their consequences, these events have terrified—have tortured—have destroyed me. Yet I will not attempt to expound them. To me they have presented little but horror—to many they still seem less terrible than *baroques*. Hereafter, perhaps, some intellect may be found which will reduce my phantasm to the commonplace—some intellect more calm, more logical, and far less excitable than my own, which will perceive, in the circumstances I detail with awe, nothing more than an ordinary succession of very natural causes and effects.

From my infancy I was noted for the docility and humanity of my disposition. My tenderness of heart was even so conspicuous as to make me the jest of my companions. I was especially fond of animals, and was indulged by my parents with a great variety of pets. With these I spent most of my time, and never was so happy as when feeding and caressing them. This peculiarity of character grew with my growth, and, in my manhood, I derived from it one of my principal sources of pleasure. To those who have cherished an affection for a faithful and sagacious dog, I need hardly be at the trouble of explaining the nature or the intensity of the gratification thus derivable. There is something in the unselfish and self-sacrificing love of a brute which goes directly to the heart of him who has had frequent occasion to test the paltry friendship and gossamer fidelity of mere *Man*.

I married early, and was happy to find in my wife a disposition not uncongenial with my own. Observing my partiality for domestic pets, she lost no opportunity of procuring those of the most agreeable kind. We had birds, gold-fish, a fine dog, rabbits, a small monkey, and *a cat*.

This latter was a remarkably large and beautiful animal, entirely black, and sagacious to an astonishing degree. In speaking of his intelligence, my wife, who at heart was not a little tinctured with superstition, made frequent allusion to the ancient popular notion, which regarded all black cats as witches in disguise. Not that she was ever *serious* upon this point—and I mention the matter at all for no better reason than that it happens, just now, to be remembered.

Pluto—this was the cat's name—was my favourite pet and playmate. I alone fed him, and he attended me wherever I went about the house. It was even with difficulty that I could prevent him from following me through the streets.

Our friendship lasted, in this manner, for several years, during which my general temperament and character—through the instrumentality of the Fiend Intemperance—had (I blush to confess it) experienced a radical alteration for the worse. I grew, day by day, more moody, more irritable, more regardless of the feelings of others. I suffered myself to use intemperate language to my wife. At length, I even offered her personal violence. My pets, of course, were

Children Playing with a Cat, Jan Mienz Molenaer (*Musée du Dunkerque*)

made to feel the change in my disposition. I not only neglected, but ill-used them. For Pluto, however, I still retained sufficient regard to restrain me from maltreating him, as I made no scruple of maltreating the rabbits, the monkey, or even the dog, when by accident, or through affection, they came in my way. But my disease grew upon me—for what disease is like Alcohol!—and at length even Pluto, who was now becoming old, and consequently somewhat peevish—even Pluto began to experience the effects of my ill-temper.

One night, returning home, much intoxicated, from one of my haunts about town, I fancied that the cat avoided my presence. I seized him: when, in his fright at my violence, he inflicted a slight wound upon my hand with his teeth. The fury of a demon instantly possessed me. I knew myself no longer. My original soul seemed, at once, to take its flight from my body; and a more than fiendish malevolence, gin-nurtured, thrilled every fibre of my frame. I took from my waistcoat pocket a pen-knife, opened it, grasped the poor beast by the throat, and deliberately cut one of its eyes from the socket! I blush, I burn, I shudder, while I pen the damnable atrocity.

When reason returned with the morning—when I had slept off the fumes of the night's debauch—I experienced a sentiment half of horror, half of remorse, for the crime of which I had been guilty: but it was, at best, a feeble and equivocal feeling, and the soul remained untouched. I again plunged into excess, and soon drowned in wine all memory of the deed.

In the meantime the cat slowly recovered. The socket of the lost eye presented, it is true, a frightful appearance, but he no longer appeared to suffer any pain. He went about the house as usual, but, as might be expected, fled in extreme terror at my approach. I had so much of my old heart left as to be at first grieved by this evident dislike on the part of a creature which had once so loved me. But this feeling soon gave place to irritation. And then came, as if to my final and irrevocable overthrow, the spirit of PERVERSENESS. Of this spirit philosophy takes no account. Yet I am not more sure that my soul lives, than I am that perverseness is one of the primitive impulses of the human heart—one of the indivisible primary faculties, or sentiments, which give direction to the character of Man. Who has not, a hundred times, found himself committing a vile or a silly action for no other reason than because he knows he should *not*? Have we not a perpetual inclination, in the teeth of our last judgment, to violate that which is *Law*, merely because we understand it to be such? This spirit of perverseness, I say, came to my final overthrow. It was this unfathomable longing of the soul to *vex itself*—to offer violence to its own nature—to do wrong for the wrong's sake only—that urged me to continue and finally to consummate the injury I had inflicted upon the unoffending brute. One morning, in cold blood, I slipped a noose about its neck and hung it to the limb of a tree—hung it with the tears streaming from my eyes, and with the bitterest remorse at my heart; hung it *because* I knew that it had loved me, and *because* I felt it had given me no reason of offence; hung it *because* I knew that in so doing I was committing a sin—a deadly sin that would so jeopardise my immortal soul as to place it—if such a thing were possible—even beyond the reach of the infinite mercy of the Most Merciful and Most Terrible God.

On the night of the day on which this cruel deed was done, I was aroused from sleep by the cry of fire. The curtains of my bed were in flames. The whole house was blazing. It was with great difficulty that my wife, a servant, and myself made our escape from the conflagration. The destruction was complete. My entire worldly wealth was swallowed up, and I resigned myself thenceforward to despair.

I am above the weakness of seeking to establish a sequence of cause and effect, between the disaster and the atrocity. But I am detailing a chain of facts—and wish not to leave even a possible link imperfect. On the day succeeding the fire, I visited the ruins. The walls, with one exception, had fallen in. This exception was found in a compartment wall, not very thick, which stood about the middle of the house, and against which had rested the head of my bed. The plastering had here, in great measure, resisted the action of the fire—a fact which I attributed to its having been recently spread. About this wall a dense crowd were collected, and many persons seemed to be examining a particular portion of it with very minute and eager attention. The words "strange!" "singular!" and other similar expressions excited my curiosity. I approached and saw, as if graven in bas-relief upon the white surface, the figure of a gigantic *cat*. The impression was given with an accuracy truly marvellous. There was a rope about the animal's neck.

When I first beheld this apparition—for I could scarcely regard it as less—my wonder and my terror were extreme. But at length reflection came to my aid. The cat, I remember, had been hung in a garden adjacent to the house. Upon the alarm of fire, this garden had been immediately filled by the crowd—by someone of whom the animal must have been cut from the tree and thrown, through an open window, into my chamber. This had probably been done with the view of arousing me from sleep. The falling of other walls had compressed the victim of my cruelty into the substance of the freshly spread plaster: the lime of which with the flames, and the *ammonia* from the carcass, had then accomplished the portraiture as I saw it.

Although I thus readily accounted to my reason, if not altogether to my conscience, for the startling fact just detailed, it did not the less fail to make a deep impression upon my fancy. For months I could not rid myself of the phantasm of the cat; and, during this period, there came back into my spirit a half-sentiment that seemed, but was not, remorse. I went so far as to regret the loss of the animal, and to look about me, among the vile haunts which I now habitually frequented, for another pet of the same species, and of somewhat similar appearance, with which to supply its place.

One night as I sat, half stupefied, in a den of more than infamy, my attention was suddenly drawn to some black object, reposing upon the head of one of the immense hogsheads of gin, or of rum, which constituted the chief furniture of the apartment. I had been looking steadily at the top of this hogshead for some minutes, and what now caused me surprise was the fact that I had not sooner perceived the object thereupon. I approached it, and touched it with my hands. It was a black cat—a very large one—fully as large as Pluto, and closely resembling him in every respect but one. Pluto had not a white hair upon any portion of his body; but this cat had a large, although indefinite splotch of white, covering nearly the whole region of the breast.

Upon my touching him, he immediately arose, purred loudly, rubbed against my hand, and appeared delighted with my notice. This, then, was the very creature of which I was in search. I at once offered to purchase it of the landlord; but this person made no claim to it—knew nothing of it—had never seen it before.

I continued my caresses, and when I prepared to go home, the animal evinced a disposition to accompany me. I permitted it to do so; occasionally stopping and patting it as I proceeded. When it reached the house it domesticated itself at once, and became immediately a great favourite with my wife.

For my own part, I soon found a dislike to it arising within me. This was just the reverse of what I had anticipated; but—I know not how or why it was—its evident fondness for myself rather disgusted and annoyed. By slow degrees, these feelings of disgust and annoyance rose into the bitterness of hatred. I avoided the creature; a certain sense of shame, and the remembrance of my former deed of cruelty, preventing me from physically abusing it. I did not, for some weeks, strike or otherwise violently ill-use it; but gradually—very gradually—I came to look upon it with unutterable loathing, and to flee silently from its odious presence, as from the breath of a pestilence.

Portrait of Girl with Cat, Charles Chaplin (*Château de Compiègne*)

What added, no doubt, to my hatred of the beast was the discovery, on the morning after I brought it home, that, like Pluto, it also had been deprived of one of its eyes. This circumstance, however, only endeared it to my wife, who, as I have already said, possessed, in a high degree, that humanity of feeling which had once been my distinguishing trait, and the source of many of my simplest and purest pleasures.

With my aversion to this cat, however, its partiality for myself seemed to increase. It followed my footsteps with a pertinacity which it would be difficult to make the reader comprehend. Whenever I sat, it would crouch beneath my chair, or spring upon my knees, covering me with its loathsome caresses. If I arose to walk, it would get between my feet, and thus nearly throw me down, or, fastening its long and sharp claws in my dress, clamber, in this manner, to my breast. At such times, although I longed to destroy it with a blow, I was yet witheld from so doing, partly by a memory of my former crime, but chiefly—let me confess it at once—by absolute *dread* of the beast.

This dread was not exactly a dread of physical evil—and yet I should be at a loss how otherwise to define it. I am almost ashamed to own—yes, even in this felon's cell, I am almost ashamed to own—that the terror and horror with which the animal inspired me had been heightened by one of the merest chimeras it would be possible to conceive. My wife had called my attention, more than once, to the character of the mark of white hair, of which I have spoken, and which constituted the sole visible difference between the strange beast and the one I had destroyed. The reader will remember that this mark, although large, had been originally very indefinite; but, by slow degrees—degrees almost imperceptible, and which for a long time my reason struggled to reject as fanciful—it had, at length, assumed the rigorous distinctness of outline. It was now the representation of an object that I shudder to name—and for this, above all, I loathed and dreaded, and would have rid myself of the monster *had I dared*—it was now, I say, the image of a hideous—of a ghastly thing—of the GALLOWS!—oh, mournful and terrible engine of Horror and of Crime—of Agony and of Death!

And now was I indeed wretched beyond the wretchedness of mere Humanity. And *a brute beast*—whose fellow I had contemptuously destroyed—*a brute beast* to work out for *me*—for me a man, fashioned in the image of the High God—so much of insufferable woe! Alas! neither by day nor by night knew I the blessing of Rest any more! During the former the creature left me no moment alone; and, in the latter, I started, hourly, from dreams of unutterable fear, to find the hot breath of *the thing* upon my face, and its vast weight—an incarnate Nightmare that I had no power to shake off—incumbent eternally upon my *heart!*

Beneath the pressure of torments such as these, the feeble remnant of the good within me succumbed. Evil thoughts became my sole intimates—the darkest and most evil of thoughts. The moodiness of my usual temper increased to hatred of all things and of all mankind; while, for the sudden, frequent, and ungovernable outbursts of a fury to which I now blindly abandoned myself, my uncomplaining wife, alas! was the most usual and the most patient of sufferers.

One day she accompanied me, upon some household errand, into the cellar of the old building which our poverty compelled us to inhabit. The cat followed me down the steep stairs, and, nearly throwing me headlong, exasperated me to madness. Uplifting an axe, and forgetting in my wrath, the childish dread which had hitherto stayed my hand, I aimed a blow at the animal which, of course, would have proved instantly fatal had it descended as I wished. But this blow was arrested by the hand of my wife. Goaded by the interference into a rage more than demoniacal, I withdrew my arm from her grasp and buried the axe in her brain. She fell dead upon the spot, without a groan.

This hideous murder accomplished, I set myself forthwith, and with entire deliberation, to

The Distressed Poet, William Hogarth

the task of concealing the body. I knew that I could not remove it from the house, either by day or by night, without the risk of being observed by the neighbours. Many projects entered my mind. At one period I thought of cutting the corpse into minute fragments, and destroying them by fire. At another, I resolved to dig a grave for it in the floor of the cellar. Again, I deliberated about casting it in the well in the yard—about packing it in a box, as if merchandise, with the usual arrangements, and so getting a porter to take it from the house. Finally I hit upon what I considered a far better expedient than either of these. I determined to wall it up in the cellar —as the monks of the Middle Ages are recorded to have walled up their victims.

For a purpose such as this the cellar was well adapted. Its walls were loosely constructed, and had lately been plastered throughout with a rough plaster, which the dampness of the atmosphere had prevented from hardening. Moreover, in one of the walls was a projection caused by a false chimney or fireplace, that had been filled up, and made to resemble the rest of the cellar. I made no doubt that I could readily displace the bricks at this point, insert the corpse, and wall the whole up as before, so that no eye could detect anything suspicious.

And in this calculation I was not deceived. By means of a crow-bar I easily dislodged the bricks, and, having carefully deposited the body against the inner wall, I propped it in that position, while, with little trouble, I re-laid the whole structure as it originally stood. Having procured mortar, sand, and hair, with every possible precaution, I prepared a plaster which could not be distinguished from the old, and with this I very carefully went over the new brick-work. When I had finished I felt satisfied that all was right. The wall did not present the slightest appearance of having been disturbed. The rubbish on the floor was picked up with the minutest care. I looked around triumphantly, and said to myself: "Here, at least, then, my labour has not been in vain."

My next step was to look for the beast which had been the cause of so much wretchedness, for I had, at length, firmly resolved to put it to death. Had I been able to meet with it, at the moment, there could have been no doubt of its fate; but it appeared that the crafty animal had been alarmed at the violence of my previous anger, and forbore to present itself in my present mood. It is impossible to describe, or to imagine, the deep, the blissful sense of relief which the absence of the detested creature occasioned in my bosom. It did not make its appearance during the night—and thus for one night at least, since its introduction into the house, I soundly and tranquilly slept; aye, *slept*, even with the burden of murder upon my soul!

The second and third day passed, and still my tormentor came not. Once again I breathed as a free man. The monster, in terror, had fled the premises for ever! I should behold it no more! My happiness was supreme! The guilt of my dark deed disturbed me but little. Some few inquiries had been made, but these had been readily answered. Even a search had been instituted—but, of course, nothing was to be discovered. I looked upon my future felicity as secured.

Upon the fourth day of the assassination, a party of the police came, very unexpectedly, into the house, and proceeded again to make rigorous investigation of the premises. Secure, however, in the inscrutability of my place of concealment, I felt no embarrassment whatever. The officers bade me accompany them in their search. They left no nook or corner unexplored. At length, for the third or fourth time, they descended into the cellar. I quivered not in a muscle. My heart beat calmly as that of one who slumbers in innocence. I walked the cellar from end to end. I folded my arms upon my bosom, and roamed easily to and fro. The police were thoroughly satisfied, and prepared to depart. The glee at my heart was too strong to be restrained. I burned to say if but one word, by way of triumph, and to render doubly sure their assurance of my guiltlessness.

"Gentlemen," I said at last, as the party ascended the steps, "I delight to have allayed your suspicions. I wish you all health and a little more courtesy. By the by, gentlemen, this—this is a very well-constructed house."—(In the rabid desire to say something easily, I scarcely knew what I uttered at all.)—"I may say an *excellently* well-constructed house. These walls—are you going, gentlemen?—these walls are solidly put together"; and here, through the mere frenzy of bravado, I rapped heavily with a cane, which I held in my hand, upon that very portion of the brick-work behind which stood the corpse of the wife of my bosom.

But may God shield and deliver me from the fangs of the Arch-Fiend! No sooner had the reverberation of my blows sunk into silence, than I was answered by a voice from within the tomb!—by a cry, at first muffled and broken, like the sobbing of a child, and then quickly swelling into one long, loud, and continous scream, utterly anomalous and inhuman—a howl—a wailing shriek, half of horror and half of triumph, such as might have arisen only out of hell, conjointly from the throats of the damned in their agony and of the demons that exult in the damnation.

Of my own thoughts it is folly to speak. Swooning, I staggered to the opposite wall. For one instant the party upon the stairs remained motionless, through extremity of terror and of awe. In the next, a dozen stout arms were toiling at the wall. It fell bodily. The corpse, already greatly decayed and clotted with gore, stood erect before the eyes of the spectators. Upon its head, with red extended mouth and solitary eye of fire, sat the hideous beast whose craft had seduced me into murder, and whose informing voice had consigned me to the hangman! I had walled the monster up within the tomb!

The Black Cat, Harry Clarke

VII

Cat's Age

The Kitten

Ogden Nash

The trouble with a kitten is
THAT
Eventually it becomes a
CAT.

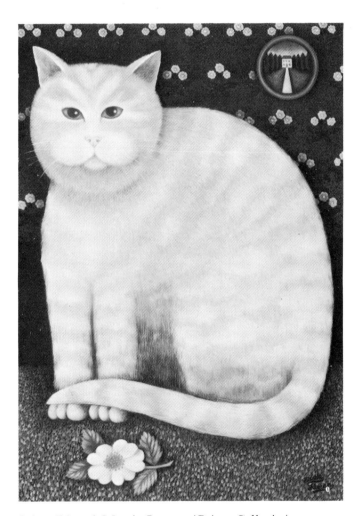

Prince Edward, Martin Leman (*Private Collection*)

Memoir of the Cats
of Greta Hall

Robert Southey

For as much, most excellent Edith May, as you must always feel a natural and becoming concern in whatever relates to the house wherein you were born, and in which the first part of your life has thus far so happily been spent, I have for your instruction and delight composed these Memoirs of the Cats of Greta Hall: to the end that the memory of such worthy animals may not perish, but be held in deserved honour by my children, and those who shall come after them. And let me not be supposed unmindful of Beelzebub of Bath, and Senhor Thomas de Lisboa, that I have not gone back to an earlier period, and included them in my design. Far be it from me to intend any injury or disrespect to their shades! Opportunity of doing justice to their virtues will not be wanting at some future time, but for the present I must confine myself within the limits of these precincts.

In the autumn of the year 1803, when I entered upon this place of abode, I found the hearth

The Woman and the Mouse, Martin Drolling (*Musée des Beaux-Arts, Orléans*)

in possession of two cats, whom my nephew Hartley Coleridge (then in the 7th year of his age) had named Lord Nelson, and Bona Marietta. The former, as the name implies, was of the worthier gender: it is as decidely so in Cats, as in Grammar and in law. He was an ugly specimen of the streaked-carrotty, or Judas-coloured kind; which is one of the ugliest varieties. But nimium ne crede colori. In spite of his complexion, there was nothing treacherous about him. He was altogether a good Cat, affectionate, vigilant and brave; and for services performed against the Rats was deservedly raised in succession to the rank of Baron, Viscount and Earl. He lived to a good old age; and then, being quite helpless and miserable, was in mercy thrown into the river. I had more than once interfered to save him from this fate; but it became at length plainly an act of compassion to consent to it. And here let me observe that in a world wherein death is necessary, the law of nature by which one creature preys upon another is a law of mercy, not only because death is thus made instrumental to life, and more life exists in consequence, but also because it is better for the creatures themselves to be cut off suddenly, than to perish by disease or hunger—for these are the only alternatives.

There are still some of Lord Nelson's descendants in the town of Keswick. Two of the family were handsomer than I should have supposed any Cats of this complexion could have been; but their fur was fine, the colour a rich carrot, and the striping like that of the finest tyger or tabby kind. I named one of them William Rufus; the other Danayr le Roux, after a personage in the Romance of Gyron le Courtoys.

Bona Marietta was the mother of Bona Fidelia, so named by my nephew aforesaid. Bona Fidelia was a tortoiseshell cat. She was filiated upon Lord Nelson, others of the same litter having borne the unequivocal stamp of his likeness. It was in her good qualities that she resembled him, for in truth her name rightly bespoke her nature. She approached as nearly as possible in disposition, to the ideal of a perfect cat: he who supposes that animals have not their difference of disposition as well as men, knows very little of animal nature. Having survived her daughter Madame Catalani, she died of extreme old age, universally esteemed and regretted by all who had the pleasure of her acquaintance.

Bona Fidelia left a daughter and a granddaughter; the former I called Madame Bianchi— the latter Pulcheria. It was impossible ever to familiarise Madame Bianchi, though she had been bred in all respects like her gentle mother, in the same place, and with the same persons. The nonsense of that arch-philosophist Helvétius would be sufficiently confuted by this single example, if such rank folly, contradicted as it is by the experience of every family, needed confutation. She was a beautiful and singular creature, white, with a fine tabby tail, and two or three spots of tabby, always delicately clean; and her wild eyes were bright and green as the Duchess de Cadaval's emerald necklace. Pulcheria did not correspond as she grew up to the promise of her kittenhood and her name; but she was as fond as her mother was shy and intractable. Their fate was extraordinary as well as mournful. When good old Mrs Wilson died, who used to feed and indulge them, they immediately forsook the house, nor could they be allured to enter it again, though they continued to wander and moan round it, and came for food. After some weeks Madame Bianchi disappeared, and Pulcheria soon afterwards died of a disease endemic at that time among cats.

For a considerable time afterwards, an evil fortune attended all our attempts at reestablishing a Cattery. Ovid disappeared and Virgil died of some miserable distemper. You and your cousin are answerable for these names: the reasons which I could find for them were, in the former case the satisfactory one that the same Ovid might be presumed to be a master in the Art of Love; and in the latter, the probable one that something like Ma-ro might be detected in the said Virgil's notes of courtship.

There was poor Othello: most properly named, for black he was, and jealous undoubtedly he would have been, but he in his kittenship followed Miss Wilbraham into the street, and there in all likelihood came to an untimely end. There was the Zombi—(I leave the Commentators to explain that title, and refer them to my History of Brazil to do it)—his marvellous story was recorded in a letter to Bedford—and after that adventure he vanished. There was Prester John, who turned out not to be of John's gender, and therefore had the name altered to Pope Joan. The Pope I am afraid came to a death of which other Popes have died. I suspect that some poison which the rats had turned out of their holes, proved fatal to their enemy. For some time I feared we were at the end of our Cat-a-logue: but at last Fortune as if to make amends for her late severity sent us two at once—the never-to-be-enough-praised Rumpelstilzchen, and the equally-to-be-admired Hurlyburlybuss.

Strange Contents, Sal Meijer (*Stedelijk Museum, Amsterdam*)

And "first for the first of these" as my huge favourite and almost namesake Robert South, says in his Sermons.

When the Midgeleys went away from the next house, they left this creature to our hospitality, cats being the least movable of all animals because of their strong local predilections; they are indeed in a domesticated state the serfs of the animal creation, and properly attached to the soil. The change was gradually and therefore easily brought about, for he was already acquainted with the children and with me; and having the same precincts to prowl in was hardly sensible of any other difference in his condition than that of obtaining a name; for when he was consigned to us he was an anonymous cat; and I having just related at breakfast with universal applause the story of Rumpelstilzchen from a German tale in Grimm's Collection, gave him that strange and magnisonant appellation; to which upon its being ascertained that he came when a kitten from a bailiff's house, I added the patronymic of Macbum. Such is his history, his character may with most propriety be introduced after the manner of Plutarch's parallels when I shall have given some previous account of his great compeer and rival Hurlyburlybuss—that name also is of Germanic and Grimmish extraction.

Whence Hurlyburlybuss came was a mystery when you departed from the Land of Lakes, and a mystery it long remained. He appeared here, as Mango Gapac did in Peru, and Quetzalcohuatl among the Aztecas, no one knew from whence. He made himself acquainted with all the philofelists of the family—attaching himself more particularly to Mrs Lovell, but he never attempted to enter the house, frequently disappeared for days, and once since my return for so long a time that he was actually believed to be dead and veritably lamented as such. The wonder was whither did he retire at such times—and to whom did he belong; for neither I in my daily walks, nor the children, nor any of the servants ever by any chance saw him anywhere except in our own domain. There was something so mysterious in this, that in old times it might have excited strong suspicion, and he would have been in danger of passing for a Witch in disguise, or a familiar. The mystery however was solved about four weeks ago, when as we were returning from a walk up the Greta, Isabel saw him on his transit across the road and the wall from Shulicrow in a direction towards the Hill. But to this day we are ignorant who has the honour to be his owner in the eye of the law; and the owner is equally ignorant of the high honour in which Hurlyburlybuss is held, of the heroic name which he has obtained, and that his fame has extended far and wide—even unto Norwich in the East, and Escott and Crediton and Kellerton in the West, yea—that with Rumpelstilzchen he has been celebrated in song, by some hitherto undiscovered poet, and that his glory will go down to future generations.

The strong enmity which unhappily subsists between these otherwise gentle and most amiable cats, is not unknown to you. Let it be imputed, as in justice it ought, not to their individual characters (for Cats have characters—and for the benefit of philosophy, as well as felisophy, this truth ought generally to be known) but to the constitution of Cat nature—an original sin, or an original necessity, which may be only another mode of expressing the same thing:

> Two stars keep not their motion in one sphere,
> Nor can one purlieu brook a double reign
> Of Hurlyburlybuss and Rumpelstilzchen.

When you left us, the result of many a fierce conflict was that Hurly remained master of the green and garden, and the whole of the out of door premises, Rumpel always upon the appearance of his victorious enemy retiring into the house as a citadel or sanctuary. The conqueror was perhaps in part indebted for this superiority to his hardier habits of life, living always in the open air, and providing for himself; while Rumpel (who though born under a bum-bailiff's roof was nevertheless kittened with a silver spoon in his mouth) past his hours in luxurious repose beside the fire, and looked for his meals as punctually as any two-legged member of the family. Yet I believe that the advantage on Hurly's side is in a great degree constitutional also, and that his superior courage arises from a confidence in his superior strength, which as you well know is visible in his make. What Benito and Maria Rosa used to say of my poor Thomaz, that he was muito hidalgo is true of Rumpelstilzchen, his countenance, deportment and behaviour being such that he is truly a gentleman-like Tom-cat. Far be it from me to praise him beyond his deserts—he is not beautiful, the mixture, tabby and white, is not good (except under very

Night Meeting, photo A. Eidenbenz (*Frank W. Lane*)

favourable combinations) and the tabby is not good of its kind. Nevertheless he is a fine cat, handsome enough for his sex, large, well-made, with good features, and an intelligent countenance, and carrying a splendid tail, which in Cats and Dogs is undoubtedly the seat of honour. His eyes which are soft and expressive are of a hue between chrysolite and emerald. Hurlyburlybuss's are between chrysolite and topaz. Which may be the more esteemed shade for the olho de gato I am not lapidary enough to decide. You should ask my Uncle. But both are of the finest water. In all his other features Hurly must yield the palm, and in form also; he has no pretensions to elegance, his size is ordinary and his figure bad: but the character of his face and neck is so masculine, that the Chinese, who use the word bull as synonymous with male, and call a boy a bull-child, might with great propriety denominate him a bull-cat. His make evinces such decided marks of strength and courage that if cat-fighting were as fashionable as cock-fighting, no cat would stand a fairer chance of winning a Welsh main. He would become as famous as the Dog Billy himself, whom I look upon as the most distinguished character that has appeared since Buonaparte.

Some weeks ago Hurlyburlybuss was manifestly emaciated and enfeebled by ill health, and Rumpelstilzchen with great magnanimity made overtures of peace. The whole progress of the treaty was seen from the parlour window. The caution with which Rumpel made his advances, the sullen dignity with which they were received, their mutual uneasiness when Rumpel, after a slow and wary approach, seated himself whisker-to-whisker with his rival, the mutual fear which restrained not only teeth and claws, but even all tones of defiance, the mutual agitation of their tails which, though they did not expand with anger, could not be kept still for suspense, and lastly the manner in which Hurly retreated, like Ajax still keeping his face towards his old antagonist, were worthy to have been represented by that painter who was called the Rafaelle of Cats. The overture I fear was not accepted as generously as it was made; for no sooner had Hurlyburlybuss recovered strength than hostilities were recommenced with greater violence than ever, Rumpel who had not abused his superiority while he possessed it, had acquired meantime a confidence which made him keep the field. Dreadful were the combats which ensued, as their ears, faces and legs bore witness. Rumpel had a wound which went through one of his feet. The result had been so far in his favour that he no longer seeks to avoid his enemy, and we are often compelled to interfere and separate them. Oh it is awful to hear the "dreadful note of preparation" with which they prelude their encounters!—the long low growl slowly rises and swells till it becomes a high sharp yowl—and then it is snapt short by a sound which seems as if they were spitting fire and venom at each other. I could half persuade myself that the word felonious is derived from the feline temper as displayed at such times. All means of reconciling them and making them understand how goodly a thing it is for cats to dwell together in peace, and what fools they are to quarrel and tear each other, are in vain. The proceedings of the Society for the Abolition of War are not more utterly ineffectual and hopeless.

All we can do is to act more impartially than the Gods did between Achilles and Hector, and continue to treat both with equal regard.

And thus having brought down these Memoirs of the Cats of Greta Hall to the present day, I commit the precious memorial to your keeping, and I remain

> Most dissipated and light-heeled daughter,
> Your most diligent and light-hearted father,
>   Robert Southey

Keswick, 18th June 1824

Sermons in Cats

Aldous Huxley

I met, not long ago, a young man who aspired to become a novelist. Knowing that I was in the profession, he asked me to tell him how he should set to work to realise his ambition. I did my best to explain. "The first thing," I said, "is to buy quite a lot of paper, a bottle of ink, and a pen. After that you merely have to write." But this was not enough for my young friend. He seemed to have a notion that there was some sort of esoteric cookery book, full of literary recipes, which you had only to follow attentively to become a Dickens, a Henry James, a Flaubert— "according to taste," as the authors of recipes say, when they come to the question of seasoning and sweetening. Wouldn't I let him have a glimpse of this cookery book? I said that I was sorry, but that (unhappily—for what an endless amount of time and trouble it would save!) I had never even seen such a work. He seemed sadly disappointed; so, to console the poor lad, I advised him to apply to the professors of dramaturgy and short-story writing at some reputable university; if any one possessed a trustworthy cookery book of literature, it should surely be they. But even this was not enough to satisfy the young man. Disappointed in his hope that I would give him the fictional equivalent of "One Hundred Ways of Cooking Eggs" or the "Carnet de la Menagère", he began to cross-examine me about my methods of "collecting material". Did I keep a notebook or a daily journal? Did I systematically frequent the drawing-rooms of the rich and fashionable? Or did I, on the contrary, inhabit the Sussex downs? Or spend my evenings looking for "copy" in East End gin-palaces? Did I think it was wise to frequent the company of intellectuals? Was it a good thing for a writer of novels to try to be well educated, or should he confine his reading exclusively to other novels? And so on. I did my best to reply to these questions—as non-commitally, of course, as I could. And as the young man still looked rather disappointed, I volunteered a final piece of advice, gratuitously. "My young friend," I said, "if you want to be a psychological novelist and write about human beings, the best thing you can do is to keep a pair of cats." And with that I left him.

Cats

I hope, for his own sake, that he took my advice. For it was good advice—the fruit of much experience and many meditations. But I am afraid that, being a rather foolish young man, he merely laughed at what he must have supposed was only a silly joke: laughed, as I myself foolishly laughed when, years ago, that charming and talented and extraordinary man, Ronald Firbank, once told me that he wanted to write a novel about life in Mayfair and so was just off to the West Indies to look for copy among the Negroes. I laughed at the time; but I see now that he was quite right. Primitive people, like children and animals, are simply civilised people with the lid off, so to speak—the heavy elaborate lid of manners, conventions, traditions of thought and feeling beneath which each one of us passes his or her existence. This lid can be very conveniently studied in Mayfair, shall we say, or Passy, or Park Avenue. But what goes on underneath the lid in these polished and elegant districts? Direct observation (unless we happen to be endowed with a very penetrating intuition) tells us but little; and, if we cannot infer what is going on under the other lids from what we see, introspectively, by peeping under our own, then the best thing we can do is to take the next boat for the West Indies, or else, less expensively, pass a few mornings in the nursery, or alternatively, as I suggested to my literary young friend, buy a pair of cats.

Yes, a pair of cats. Siamese by preference; for they are certainly the most "human" of all the race of cats. Also the strangest, and, if not the most beautiful, certainly the most striking and fantastic. For what disquieting pale blue eyes stare out from the black velvet masks of their faces! Snow-white at birth, their bodies gradually darken to a rich mulatto colour. Their forepaws are gloved almost to the shoulder like the long black kid arms of Yvette Guilbert; over their hind legs are tightly drawn the black silk stockings with which Félicien Rops so perversely and indecently clothed his pearly nudes. Their tails, when they have tails—and I would always recommend the budding novelist buy the tailed variety; for the tail, in cats, is the principal organ of emotional expression and a Manx cat is the equivalent of a dumb man—their tails are tapering black serpents endowed, even when the body lies in Sphinx-like repose, with a spasmodic and uneasy life of their own. And what strange voices they have! Sometimes like the complaining of small children; sometimes like the noise of lambs; sometimes like the agonised and furious howling of lost-souls. Compared with these fantastic creatures, other cats, however beautiful and engaging, are apt to seem a little insipid.

Well, having bought his cats, nothing remains for the would-be novelist but to watch them living from day to day; to mark, learn, and inwardly digest the lessons about human nature which they teach; and finally—for, alas, this arduous and unpleasant necessity always arises—finally write his book about Mayfair, Passy, or Park Avenue, whichever the case may be.

Let us consider some of these instructive sermons in cats, from which the student of human psychology can learn so much. We will begin—as every good novel should begin, instead of absurdly ending—with marriage. The marriage of Siamese cats, at any rate as I have observed it, is an extraodinarily dramatic event. To begin with, the introduction of the bridegroom to his bride (I am assuming that, as usually happens in the world of cats, they have not met before their wedding day) is the signal for a battle of unparalleled ferocity. The young wife's first reaction to the advances of her would-be husband is to fly at his throat. One is thankful, as one watches the fur flying and listens to the piercing yells of rage and hatred, that a kindly providence has not allowed these devils to grow any larger. Waged between creatures as big as men, such battles would bring death and destruction to everything within a radius of hundreds of yards. As things are, one is able, at the risk of a few scratches, to grab them, still writhing and spitting, apart. What would happen if the newly-wedded pair were allowed to go on fighting to the bitter end I do not know, and have never had the scientific curiosity or the strength of mind to try to find out. I suspect that, contrary to what happened in Hamlet's family, the wedding baked meats would soon be serving for a funeral. I have always prevented this tragical consummation by simply shutting up the bride in a room by herself and leaving the bride-groom for a few hours to languish outside the door. He does not languish dumbly; but for a long time there is no answer, save an occasional hiss or growl, to his melancholy cries of love. When, finally, the bride begins replying in tones as soft and yearning as his own, the door may be opened. The bridegroom darts in and is received, not with tooth and claw as on the former occasion, but with every demonstration of affection.

At first there would seem, in this specimen of feline behaviour, no special "message" for humanity. But appearances are deceptive; the lids under which civilised people live are so thick and so profusely sculptured with mythological ornaments, that it is difficult to recognise the fact, so much insisted upon by D. H. Lawrence in his novels and stories, that there is almost always a mingling of hate with the passion of love and that young girls very often feel (in spite of their sentiments and even their desires) a real abhorrence of the fact of physical love. Unlidded, the cats make manifest this ordinary obscure mystery of human behaviour. After witnessing a cats' wedding no young novelist can rest content with the falsehood and banalities which pass, in current fiction, for descriptions of love.

Time passes and, their honeymoon over, the cats begin to tell us things about humanity which even the lid of civilisation cannot conceal in the world of men. They tell us—what, alas, we already know—that husbands soon tire of their wives, particularly when they are expecting or nursing families; that the essence of maleness is the love of adventure and infidelity; that guilty consciences and good resolutions are the psychological symptoms of that disease which spasmodically affects practically every male between the ages of eighteen and sixty—the disease called "the morning after"; and that with the disappearance of the disease the psychological symptoms also disappear, so that when temptation comes again, conscience is dumb and good resolutions count for nothing. All these unhappily too familiar truths are illustrated by the cats with a most comical absence of disguise. No man has ever dared to manifest his boredom so insolently as does a Siamese tom-cat, when he yawns in the face of his amorously importunate wife. No man has ever dared to proclaim his illicit amours so frankly as this same tom cater-wauling on the tiles. And how slinkingly—no man was ever so abject—he returns next day to the conjugal basket by the fire! You can measure the guiltiness of his conscience by the angle of his back-pressed ears, the droop of his tail. And when, having sniffed him and so discovered his infidelity, his wife, as she always does on these occasions begins to scratch his face (already scarred, like a German student's, with the traces of a hundred duels), he makes no attempt to resist; for, self-convicted of sin, he knows that he deserves all he is getting.

It is impossible for me in the space at my disposal to enumerate all the human truths which a pair of cats can reveal or confirm. I will cite only one more of the innumerable sermons in cats which my memory holds—an acted sermon which, by its ludicrous pantomime, vividly brought home to me the most saddening peculiarity of our human nature, its irreducible solitariness. The circumstances were these. My she-cat, by now a wife of long standing and several times a mother, was passing through one of her occasional phases of amorousness. Her husband, now in the prime of life and parading that sleepy arrogance which is the characteristic of the mature and conquering male (he was now the feline equivalent of some herculean young Alcibiades, of

JOHN KAY

Drawn & Engraved by Himself 1786.

John Kay and His Cat

the Guards), refused to have anything to do with her. It was in vain that she uttered her love-sick mewing, in vain that she walked up and down in front of him rubbing herself voluptuously against doors and chair legs as she passed, it was in vain that she came and licked his face. He shut his eyes, he yawned, he averted his head, or, if she became too importunate, got up and slowly, with an air of insulting dignity and detachment, stalked away. When the opportunity presented itself, he escaped and spent the next twenty-four hours upon the tiles. Left to herself, the wife went wandering disconsolately about the house, as though in search of a vanished happiness, faintly and plaintively mewing to herself in a voice and with a manner that reminded one irresistibly of Mélisande in Debussy's opera, "*Je ne suis pas heureuse ici,*" she seemed to be saying. And, poor little beast, she wasn't. But, like her big sisters and brothers of the human world, she had to bear her unhappiness in solitude, uncomprehended, unconsoled. For in spite of language, in spite of intelligence and intuition and sympathy, one can never really communicate anything to anybody. The essential substance of every thought and feeling remains incommunicable, locked up in the impenetrable strong-room of the individual soul and body. Our life is a sentence of perpetual solitary confinement. This mournful truth was overwhelmingly borne in on me as I watched the abandoned and love-sick cat as she walked un-happily round my room. "*Je ne suis pas heureuse ici,*" she kept mewing, "*je ne suis pas heureuse ici.*" And her expressive black tail would lash the air in a tragical gesture of despair. But each time it twitched, hop-la! from under the armchair, from behind the book-case, wherever he happened to be hiding at the moment, out jumped her only son (the only one, that is, we had not given away), jumped like a ludicrous toy tiger, all claws out, on to the moving tail. Sometimes he would miss, sometimes he caught it, and getting the tip between his teeth would pretend to worry it, absurdly ferocious. His mother would have to jerk it violently to get it out of his mouth. Then, he would go back under his armchair again and, crouching down, his hindquarters trembling, would prepare once more to spring. The tail, the tragical, despairingly gesticulating tail, was for him the most irresistible of playthings. The patience of the mother was angelical. There was never a rebuke or a punitive reprisal; when the child became too intolerable, she just moved away; that was all. And meanwhile, all the time, she went on mewing, plaintively, despairingly. "*Je ne suis pas heureuse ici, je ne suis pas heureuse ici.*" It was heartbreaking. The more so as the antics of the kitten were so extraordinarily ludicrous. It was as though a slap-stick comedian had broken in on the lamentations of Mélisande—not mischievously, not wittingly, for there was not the smallest intention to hurt the little cat's performance, but simply from lack of comprehension. Each was alone serving his life-sentence of solitary confinement. There was no communication from cell to cell. Absolutely no communication. These sermons in cats can be exceedingly depressing.

Fourteen Ways Of Touching The Peter

George MacBeth

I
You can push
your thumb
in the
ridge
between his
shoulder-blades
to please him.

The Two Beggars (detail), Giacomo Ceruti (*Pinacoteca Tosio Martinengo, Brescia*)

II
Starting
at its root,
you can let
his whole
tail
flow
through your hand.

III
Forming
a fist
you can let
him rub
his bone
skull
against it, hard.

[223]

IV

When he makes
bread,
you can lift
him
by his under-
sides on your
knuckles.

V

In hot
weather
you can itch
the fur
under
his chin. He
likes that.

VI

At night
you can hoist
him
out of his bean-stalk,
sleepily
clutching
paper bags.

VII

Pressing
his head against
your cheek,
you can carry
him
in the dark,
safely.

VIII

In late Autumn
you can find
seeds
adhering
to his fur.
There are
plenty.

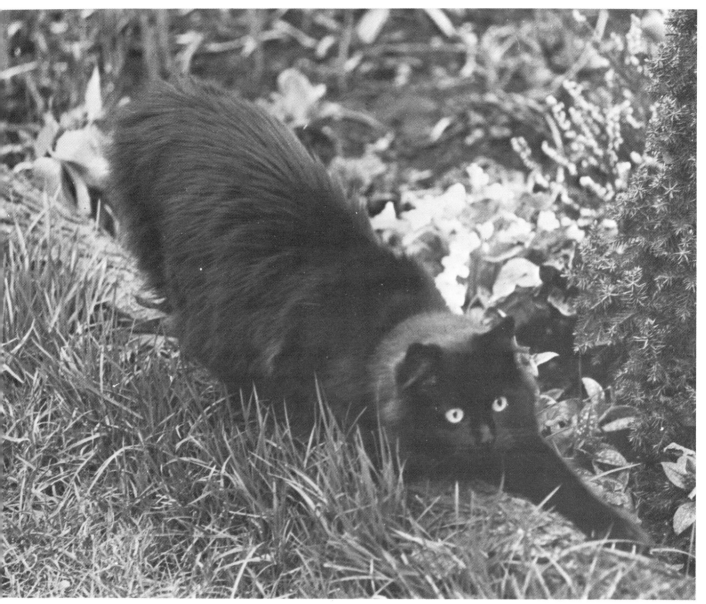

Rosie stalking, photo Simon Playle

IX
You can prise
his jaws
open,
helping
any medicine
he won't
abide, go down.

[225]

X

You can touch
his
feet, only
if
he is relaxed.
He
doesn't like it.

XI

You can comb
spare thin
fur
from his coat,
so he won't
get
fur-ball.

XII

You can shake
his rigid
chicken-leg leg,
scouring his
hind-quarters
with his Vim
tongue.

XIII

Dumping
hot fish
on his plate, you can
fend
him off,
pushing
and purring.

XIV

You can have
him shrimp
along you,
breathing,
whenever
you want
to compose poems.

Cat Writing Poem (British Library, London)

Cat

Michael Hamburger

Unfussy lodger, she knows what she wants and gets it:
Food, cushions, fires, the run of the garden.
I, her night porter in the small hours,
Don't bother to grumble, grimly let her in.
To that coldness she purrs assent,
Eats her fill and outwits me,
Plays hide and seek in the dark house.

Only at times, by chance meeting the gaze
Of her amber eyes that can rest on me
As on a beech-bole, on bracken or meadow grass
I'm moved to celebrate the years between us,
The farness and the nearness:
My fingers graze her head.
To that fondness she purrs assent.

Slumbering Cat, photo Will Green

Jeremy Bentham's Cat

Dr Bowring

Bentham was very fond of animals, particularly "pussies", as he called them, when they had domestic virtues, but he had no particular affection for the common race of cats. He had one, however, of which he used to boast that he had "made a man of him", and whom he was wont to invite to eat macaroni at his own table. This puss got knighted, and rejoiced in the name of Sir John Langbourne. In his early days he was a frisky, inconsiderate, and, to say the truth, somewhat profligate gentleman; and had, according to the report of his patron, the habit of seducing light and giddy young ladies, of his own race, into the garden of Queen's Square Place: but tired at last, like Solomon, of pleasures and vanities, he became sedate and thoughtful —took to the church, laid down his knightly title, and was installed as the Reverend John Langbourne. He gradually obtained a great reputation for sanctity and learning, and a Doctor's degree was conferred upon him. When I knew him, in his declining days, he bore no other name than the Reverend Doctor John Langbourne: and he was alike conspicuous for his gravity and philosophy. Great respect was invariably shown his reverence: and it was supposed that he was not far off from a mitre, when old age interfered with his hopes and honours. He departed amidst the regrets of his many friends, and was gathered to his fathers, and to eternal rest, in a cemetery in Milton's garden.

FROM
Wild Wales

George Borrow

As I and my family sat at tea in our parlour, an hour or two after we had taken possession of our lodgings, the door of the room and that of the entrance of the house being open, on account of the fineness of the weather, a poor black cat entered hastily, sat down on the carpet by the table, looked up towards us, and mewed piteously. I never had seen so wretched a looking creature. It was dreadfully attenuated, being little more than skin and bone, and was sorely afflicted with an eruptive malady. And here I may as well relate the history of this cat previous to our arrival which I subsequently learned by bits and snatches. It had belonged to a previous vicar of Llangollen, and had been left behind at his departure. His successor brought with him dogs and cats, who, conceiving that the late vicar's cat had no business at the vicarage, drove it forth to seek another home, which, however, it could not find. Almost all the people of the suburb were dissenters, as indeed were the generality of the people at Llangollen, and knowing the cat to be a church cat, not only would not harbour it, but did all they could to make it miserable; whilst the few who were not dissenters, would not receive it into their houses, either because they had cats of their own, or dogs, or did not want a cat, so that the cat had no home and was dreadfully persecuted by nine-tenths of the suburb. Oh, there never was a cat so persecuted as that poor Church of England animal, and solely on account of the opinions which it was supposed to have imbibed in the house of its late master, for I never could learn that the dissenters of the suburb, nor indeed of Llangollen in general, were in the habit of persecuting other cats; the cat was a Church of England cat, and that was enough: stone it, hang it, drown it! were the cries of almost everybody. If the workmen of the flannel factory, all of whom were Calvinistic Methodists, chanced to get a glimpse of it in the road from the windows of the building, they would sally forth in a body, and with sticks, stones, or for want of other weapons, with clots of horse-dung, of which there was always plenty on the road, would chase it up the high bank or perhaps over the Camlas—the inhabitants of a small street between our house and the factory leading from the road to the river, all of whom were dissenters, if they saw it moving about the perllan, into which their back windows looked, would shriek and hoot at it, and fling anything of no value, which came easily to hand, at the head or body of the ecclesiastical cat. The good woman of the house, who though a very excellent person, was a bitter dissenter, whenever she saw it upon her ground or heard it was there, would make after it, frequently attended by her maid Margaret, and her young son, a boy about nine years of age, both of whom hated the cat,

Dog and Cat, Frantz Snyders (*Musée des Beaux-Arts, Grenoble*)

and were always ready to attack it, either alone or in company, and no wonder, the maid being not only a dissenter, but a class teacher, and the boy not only a dissenter, but intended for the dissenting ministry. Where it got its food, and food it sometimes must have got, for even a cat, an animal known to have nine lives, cannot live without food, was only known to itself, as was the place where it lay, for even a cat must lie down sometimes; though a labouring man who occasionally dug in the garden told me he believed that in the springtime it ate freshets, and the woman of the house once said that she believed it sometimes slept in the hedge, which hedge, by the bye, divided our perllan from the vicarage grounds, which were very extensive. Well might the cat having led this kind of life for better than two years look mere skin and bone when it made its appearance in our apartment, and have an eruptive malady, and also a bronchitic cough, for I remember it had both. How it came to make its appearance there is a mystery, for it had never entered the house before, even when there were lodgers; that it should not visit the woman, who was its declared enemy, was natural enough, but why, if it did not visit her other lodgers, did it visit us? Did instinct keep it aloof from them? Did instinct draw it towards us?

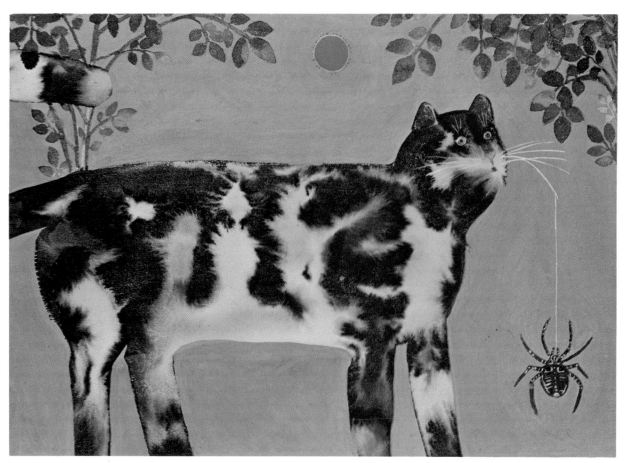

Cat with Spider, Jillian Peccinotti (*Michael Parkin Fine Art Ltd*)

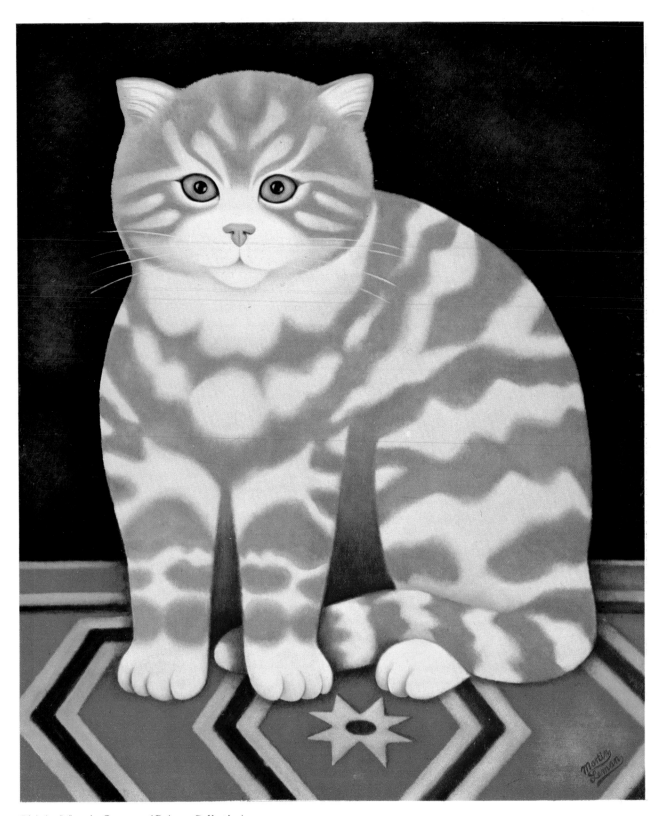

Trixie, Martin Leman (*Private Collection*)

We gave it some bread-and-butter, and a little tea with milk and sugar. It ate and drank and soon began to purr. The good woman of the house was horrified when on coming in to remove the things she saw the church cat on her carpet. "What impudence!" she exclaimed, and made towards it, but on our telling her that we did not expect that it should be disturbed, she let it alone. A very remarkable circumstance was, that though the cat had hitherto been in the habit of flying not only from her face, but the very echo of her voice, it now looked her in the face with perfect composure, as much as to say, "I don't fear you, for I know that I am now safe and with my own people." It stayed with us two hours and then went away. The next morning it returned. To be short, though it went away every night, it became our own cat, and one of our family. I gave it something which cured it of its eruption, and through good treatment it soon lost its other ailments and began to look sleek and bonny.

We were at first in some perplexity with respect to the disposal of the ecclesiastical cat; it would of course not do to leave it in the garden to the tender mercies of the Calvinistic Methodists of the neighbourhood, more especially those of the flannel manufactory, and my wife and daughter could hardly carry it with them. At length we thought of applying to a young woman of sound church principles who was lately married and lived over the water on the way to the railway station, with whom we were slightly acquainted, to take charge of the animal, and she on the first intimation of our wish willingly acceded to it. So with her poor puss was left along with a trifle for its milk-money, and with her, as we subsequently learned, it continued in peace and comfort till one morning it sprang suddenly from the hearth into the air, gave a mew and died. So much for the ecclesiastical cat.

The Cat

Robin Skelton

—for Sam—

The cat stood under the lilac.
It was black.
The sky was blue, the grass green,
and it stood
black under the lilac
that was lilac
under the sky that was all over blue.

No matter that the way we say is how
the thing is in the mind, a proof of sorts
that where we stand and look is what we are,
sometimes a black cat stands black under lilac
and the grass is green, the sky unknown.

To Mrs Reynolds' Cat

John Keats

Cat! who hast pass'd thy grand climacteric,
    How many mice and rats hast in thy days
    Destroy'd? How many tit bits stolen? Gaze
With those bright languid segments green, and prick
Those velvet ears—but pr'ythee do not stick
    Thy latent talons in me—and upraise
    Thy gentle mew—and tell me all thy frays,
Of fish and mice, and rats and tender chick.
Nay, look not down, nor lick thy dainty wrists—
    For all thy wheezy asthma—and for all
Thy tail's tip is nick'd off—and though the fists
    Of many a maid have given thee many a maul,
Still is that fur as soft, as when the lists
    In youth thou enter'dest on glass bottled wall.

On a Cat Aging

Alexander Gray

He blinks upon the hearth-rug
And yawns in deep content,
Accepting all the comforts
That Providence has sent.

Louder he purrs, and louder,
In one glad hymn of praise,
For all the night's adventures,
For quiet, restful days.

A Sleeping Maid, Nicolaes Maes (*National Gallery, London*)

Life will go on for ever,
With all that cat can wish;
Warmth, and the glad procession
Of fish, and milk and fish.

Only—the thought disturbs him—
He's noticed once or twice,
The times are somehow breeding
A nimbler race of mice.

Cat, 1804

Old Tom

Richard Eberhart

An old, black, rutting tomcat,
The brother of his female,
Expressed nature in his sister
Begetting again in his future.

I eye this old, mangy fellow
With a certain sympathy.
His progeny already
Have suffered fortune and misfortune

Teaching us, as larger animals,
Something of ourselves.
As poets will to survive,
Cats survive by force.

A kitten could not be expected
To understand a moving car.
One, atop my front wheel,
Was rolled down to mutilation.

I had to kill her with a club
And buried her in the bushes,
Shaking with the dread of this
But doing it nevertheless.

Her little brother very soon
Had caught a bird so beautiful
I hated to see it mutilated,
And left only feathers and the spleen.

They are the most civilised creatures,
Sleep all day and hunt by night,
Elegance in the drawing room,
Merciless in dusk or in moonlight.

But most it is their indifference
To death of their own fellows
I applaud; they go about their business,
Unquestioning the fates of those fellows.

Old Tom, here is a handout,
Some meal and some milk for you.
Go rough it under the stars,
You teach us what we are

When our policies are riven
And our pretensions are bare,
And we are subservient to nature
Very much as you are.

VIII

Cat's Death

My Old Cat

Hal Summers

My old cat is dead,
Who would butt me with his head.
He had the sleekest fur.
He had the blackest purr.
Always gentle with us
Was this black puss,
But when I found him today
Stiff and cold where he lay
His look was a lion's,
Full of rage, defiance:
Oh, he would not pretend
That what came was a friend
But met it in pure hate.
Well died, my old cat.

On Clem: A Cat

Geoffrey Holloway

A thing of piebald moods, true to his born colours—
querulous if shook from noonday beds
yet mornings given to nudging one awake
breathy, tickling, with stubborn tenderness . . .
not much at bouncing intruder toms
but liked to prowl for dogs, the bigger the tastier . . .
could saunter with a mannequin's rubato
but was never that feline about birds
save once: dozing on a sill
he snapped a breakneck bluetit rebounding off the pane . . .

The Cat Loves Fish . . ., Joseph Low (*Museum of Fine Arts, Boston, William A. Sargent Fund*)

We had him thirteen years.
Then something grew between:
he'd drool, subside in road-middles,
mess anywhere.
So, the vets. The last time
—oddly enough—
he purred like a sun-tuned grasshopper.
After, we couldn't open
that cardboard box—all the way back
colder, heavier—
but buried him with it.

He's there, by the garden-fence,
two sticks looped over with washing-line.
A rough job . . . like death generally . . .
but fitting somehow (he was farm stock)
and lasts, has meaning; if not perhaps
for the robin that sometimes lingers
wind-flaked, on its cross.

Dostoievsky

Robert Leach

Our cat had gone
When we returned from holiday.
A week forgetting him,
Browning our pallor miles away,

And he was gone. Walked out on us.
His alert, delicate contempt had suggested Dostoievsky,
And so I'd called him:
The name satisfied my intellectual vanity.

The kids called him Dusty
And profligated the love of youth
On him. He ignored them, preferring
To snap wasps with his red mouth,

Self-portrait 1928, Tsugouharu Foujita (*Musée Nationale d' Art Moderne, Paris*)

Eating them, stings and all. He was like that—
A baroque destroyer, researching
A library of garbage with taloned eloquence,
Minutely secret as a professor.

[242]

When we came back from the seaside
He was gone. No goodbye,
Merely an absent wish
And something to remember him by—

A pillow's worth of feathers
And two dead birds on the living-room floor,
Guts spilling from the half-open corpses like
Underclothing from a dowager's boudoir drawer.

Among the intestine clots
A million maggots wagged,
Bulbous whitey things, wriggling, squirming, gorging
In half-gore carcasses stiff like crags.

The children missed him,
Dusty, they searched and called.
He didn't come. This indifference
Was once for all.

I'd only called him Dostoievsky
Out of intellectual pride;
When Dusty went,
The children cried.

Cat, Warwick Hutton (*The Keepsake Press*)

[243]

Last Words to a
Dumb Friend

Thomas Hardy

Pet was never mourned as you
Purrer of the spotless hue,
Plumy tail, and wistful gaze
While you humoured our queer ways,
Or outshrilled your morning call
Up the stairs and through the hall—
Foot suspended in its fall—
While expectant, you would stand
Arched to meet the stroking hand;
Till your way you chose to wend
Yonder, to your tragic end.

Never another pet for me!
Let your place all vacant be;
Better blankness day by day
Than companion torn away.
Better bid his memory fade,
Better blot each mark he made,
Selfishly escape distress
By contrived forgetfulness,
Than preserve his prints to make
Every morn and eve an ache.

From the chair whereon he sat
Sweep his fur, nor wince thereat;
Rake his little pathways out
Mid the bushes roundabout;
Smooth away his talons' mark
From the claw-worn pine-tree bark,
Where he climbed as dusk embrowned,
Waiting us who loitered round.

Girl and Cat, John Russell (*Tate Gallery, London*)

Strange it is this speechless thing,
Subject to our mastering,
Subject for his life and food
To our gift, and time, and mood;
Timid pensioner of us Powers,
His existence ruled by ours,
Should—by crossing at a breath
Into safe and shielded death,
By the merely taking hence
Of his insignificance—
Loom as largened to the sense,
Shape as part, above man's will,
Of the Imperturbable.

[245]

As a prisoner, flight debarred,
Exercising in a yard,
Still retain I, troubled, shaken,
Mean estate, by him forsaken;
And this home, which scarcely took
Impress from his little look,
By his faring to the Dim
Grows all eloquent of him.

Housemate, I can think you still
Bounding to the window-sill,
Over which I vaguely see
Your small mound beneath the tree,
Showing in the autumn shade
That you moulder where you played.

In Memory of My Cat, Domino: 1951–66

Roy Fuller

Rising at dawn to pee, I thought I saw you
Curved in a chair, with head raised to look at me,
As you did at such hours. But the next moment,
More used to the gloom, there was only a jar
And a face-cloth. Time enough, nonetheless,
For love's responsibilities to return
To me.
         The unique character of the dead
Is the source of our sense of mourning and loss;
So, back in bed, I avoided calling up
What I know is intact in my mind, your life,
Entirely possessed as it was by my care.

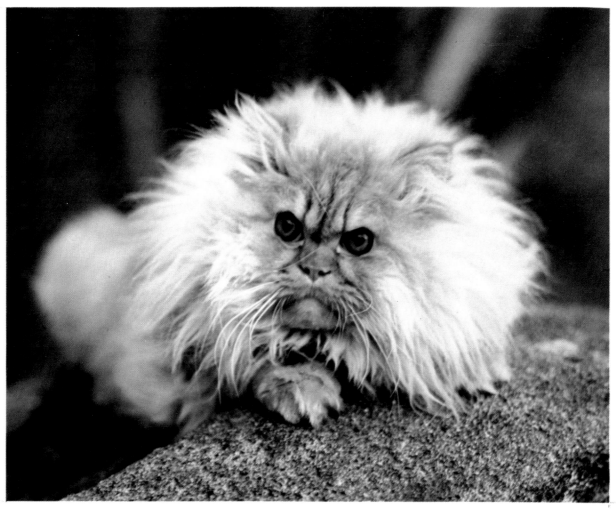

Ginger Persian Cat, photo Hans Reinhard (*Bruce Coleman Ltd*)

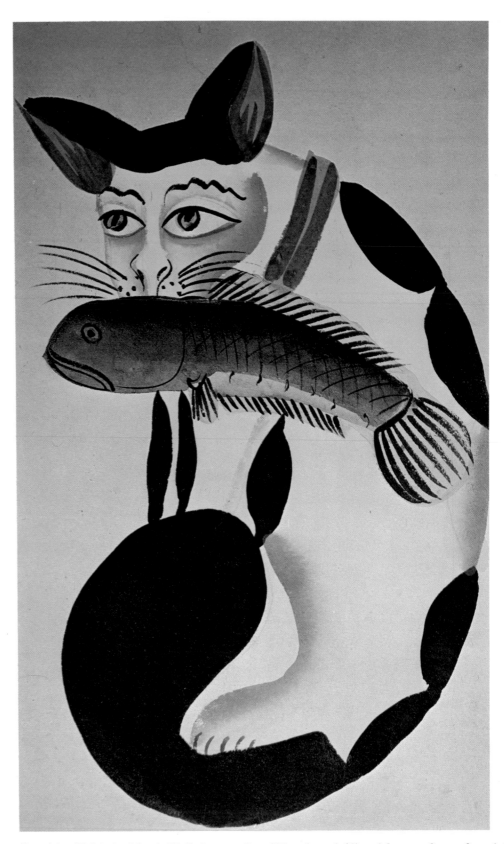

Cat with a Fish in its Mouth, Kalighat, *c.* 1890 (*Victoria and Albert Museum. Crown Copyright*)

I could conceive you not as dead but merely
Gone before me to a world that sends to us
Decreasing intimations of its beings—
No doubt because they find us in the end
Pathetic, worthy, but of small importance.

So long had we been together it never
Occurred to me I might fall somewhat behind.
Even when, familiar fur in my hands,
The sickly wave of barbiturate rose up,
I thought it was I who was journeying on—
But looking back there is only emptiness,
Your dusty medicaments and my portrait
Taken with you: sad mode of life you've outpaced.

On the Death of a Favourite Cat, Drowned in a Tub of Gold Fishes

Thomas Gray

'Twas on a lofty vase's side,
Where China's gayest art had dy'd
    The azure flowers that blow;
Demurest of the tabby kind,
The pensive Selima, reclin'd,
    Gaz'd on the lake below.

Her conscious tail her joy declar'd;
The fair round face, the snowy beard,
    The velvet of her paws,
Her coat, that with the tortoise vies,
Her ears of jet, and emerald eyes,
    She saw; and purr'd applause.

Horace Walpole's Cat, Selima

Still had she gaz'd; but 'midst the tide
Two angel forms were seen to glide,
    The Genii of the stream:
Their scaly armour's Tyrian hue
Thro' richest purple to the view
    Betray'd a golden gleam.

The hapless Nymph with wonder saw:
A whisker first, and then a claw,
    With many an ardent wish,
She stretch'd in vain to reach the prize.
What female heart can gold despise?
    What Cat's averse to fish?

Presumptuous Maid! with looks intent
Again she stretch'd, again she bent,
    Nor knew the gulf between.
(Malignant Fate sat by, and smil'd.)
The slipp'ry verge her feet beguil'd,
    She tumbled headlong in.

[248]

Eight times emerging from the flood
She mew'd to ev'ry wat'ry God,
    Some speedy aid to send.
No Dolphin came, no Nereid stirr'd:
Nor cruel *Tom*, nor *Susan* heard.
    A Fav'rite has no friend!

From hence, ye Beauties, undeceiv'd,
Know, one false step is ne'er retriev'd,
    And be with caution bold.
Not all that tempts your wand'ring eyes
And heedless hearts, is lawful prize;
    Nor all that glisters, gold.

Death of the Cat

Ian Serraillier

Alas! Mowler, the children's pride,
Has slipped on a water-butt, tumbled inside
And died.

The seamstress on her sewing machine
Stitched a shroud of satin sheen.

The carpenter hammered and planed a coffin
Of seasoned oak without a knot in.

The sexton—he loved dear Mowler well—
Mournfully, mournfully tolled the bell.

Few were the prayers the parson spoke.
All he could do, poor fellow, was choke.

But saddest of all in the funeral train
Were the children. Deep were their sorrow and pain,

For they knew, as they followed the churchyard through,
They'd never set eyes on Mowler again.

Dressing the Kitten, Joseph Wright of Derby (*The Iveagh Bequest, Kenwood*)

In silence behind the coffin they stepped,
Solemnly, slowly. Everyone wept

Except
The little mice hid in the hedge—not they!

'Twas not *their* hearts that bled.
"Let's out and play,"
They cried. "Oh, spread
The butter thick on the bread!
Dance in cream cheese right up to our knees,
For the cat is dead!
Hooray!
The cat
        is
                dead!"

Mike

Sir Ernest A. Wallis Budge

(The cat who assisted in keeping the main gate of the British Museum from
February, 1909, to January, 1929)

In the days when that famous and learned man, Sir Richard Garnett, ruled over the Department
of Printed Books in the British Museum, he was frequently visited by a cat who was generally
known among the staff as "Black Jack".

He was a very handsome black creature, with a white shirt front and white paws, and whiskers of great length. He was fond of sitting on the desks in the Reading Room, and he never
hesitated to ask a reader to hold open both folding doors when he wanted to go out into the
corridor. Being shut in one of the newspaper rooms one Sunday, and being bored, he amused
himself by sharpening his claws on the bindings of the volumes of newspapers, and it must be
confessed did much damage. This brought down upon him the wrath of the officials, and he was
banished from the library; the Clerk of the Works was ordered to get rid of him, and tried to do
so, but failed, for Black Jack had disappeared mysteriously. The truth was that two of the members of the staff arranged for him to be kept in safety in a certain place, and provided him with
food and milk. An official report was written to the effect that Black Jack had disappeared, and
he was "presumed dead"; the bindings of the volumes of newspapers were repaired, and the
official mind was once more at peace. A few weeks later Black Jack reappeared, and everyone
was delighted to see him again; and the chief officials asked no questions!

[251]

Early in the spring of 1908 the Keeper of the Egyptian Cat Mummies in the British Museum was going down the steps of his official residence, when he saw Black Jack coming towards the steps and carrying something rather large in his mouth. He came to the steps and deposited his burden on the steps at the Keeper's feet and then turned and walked solemnly away. The something which he deposited on the steps was a kitten, and that kitten was later known to fame as "Mike". The kitten was taken in and cared for and grew and flourished, and by great good luck was adopted as a pal by the two cats already in the house. So all was well.

When Mike was a little older he went and made friends with the kind-hearted gatekeeper at the main gate, and he began to frequent the lodge. By day and night he was always sure of a welcome, and thus he was the happy possessor of two homes. On Sunday mornings the house cat taught him to stalk pigeons in the colonnade. Mike was set to "point" like a dog, and the house cat little by little drove the pigeons up into a corner. The pigeons became dazed, and fell down, and then each cat seized a bird and carried it into the house uninjured. The Housekeeper took the pigeons from the cats, and in return for them gave a slice of beef or mutton and milk to each cat. The pigeons were taken into a little side room, and after they had eaten some maize and drunk water, they flew out of the window none the worse for their handling by the cats. The fact was that neither cat liked to eat game with dirty, sooty, feathers on it; they preferred clean, cooked meat.

As time went on, Mike, wishing to keep his proceedings during the hours of night uncriticised by the household, preferred the lodge to the house, and finally he took up his abode there; the corner shelf out of the draughts was prepared for him to sleep on, and he could go out and come in at any time he pleased both by day and by night. The Keeper of the Mummied Cats took care to feed him during the lean years of the war, and whoever went short, Mike did not. During the last two years he was difficult to feed because of his decaying teeth, but a diet of tender meat and fish on alternate days kept him going. He preferred sole to whiting, and whiting to haddock, and sardines to herrings; for cod he had no use whatever. He owed much to the three kind-hearted gatekeepers who cooked his food for him, and treated him as a man and a brother.

A Case of Murder

Vernon Scannell

They should not have left him there alone,
Alone that is except for the cat.
He was only nine, not old enough
To be left alone in a basement flat,
Alone, that is, except for the cat.
A dog would have been a different thing,

A big gruff dog with slashing jaws,
But a cat with round eyes mad as gold,
Plump as a cushion with tucked-in paws—
Better have left him with a fair-sized rat!
But what they did was leave him with a cat.
He hated that cat; he watched it sit,
A buzzing machine of soft black stuff,

Cat, Louis Wain (*Michael Parkin Fine Art Ltd*)

He sat and watched and he hated it,
Snug in its fur, hot blood in a muff,
And its mad gold stare and the way it sat
Crooning dark warmth: he loathed all that.
So he took Daddy's stick and he hit the cat.
Then quick as a sudden crack in glass
It hissed, black flash, to a hiding place
In the dust and dark beneath the couch,
And he followed the grin on his new-made face,
A wide-eyed, frightened snarl of a grin,
And he took the stick and he thrust it in,
Hard and quick in the furry dark.
The black fur squealed and he felt his skin

[253]

Prickle with sparks of dry delight.
Then the cat again came into sight,
Shot for the door that wasn't quite shut,
But the boy, quick too, slammed fast the door:
The cat, half-through, was cracked like a nut
And the soft black thud was dumped on the floor.
Then the boy was suddenly terrified
And he bit his knuckles and cried and cried;
But he had to do something with the dead thing there.
His eyes squeezed beads of salty prayer
But the wound of fear gaped wide and raw;
He dared not touch the thing with his hands
So he fetched a spade and shovelled it
And dumped the load of heavy fur
In the spidery cupboard under the stair
Where it's been for years, and though it died
It's grown in that cupboard and its hot low purr
Grows slowly louder year by year:
There'll not be a corner for the boy to hide
When the cupboard swells and all sides split
And the huge black cat pads out of it.

The King of the Cats
is Dead

Jeni Couzyn

The king of the cats is dead
Tom the all time conqueror
Tom the invincible bushytailed
Tom the monarch of eternity.
Hazel-eyed
he could see around the world
knew the hiding places of birds
terror of rats and squirrels he
played games on the wild heath

Cat with Bird (Museo Nazionale, Naples)

with credible pretty witches
Tom the slant-eyed
Tom the cunning deceitful trickster of men
Tom the hero among cats
Tom the wise of many generations.

Alas Tom is dead.
I sing his praises who would not have noticed
contemptible me. Alas Tom the hero
I see you everywhere, in black cats
everywhere I am looking for you
who betrayed you.
Your yellow eyes plague my vision.

The king of the cats is dead.
They are building the Royal Free
where he ruled generations of cats who were
knights among cats, the round table of
noble cats, the merry men among cats

scorning the dandy domestics.
Wildcat of dustbin and midnight
they were sovereign
where whitecoated men lurk now in the
old places, scum of the earth with your nets and
poised syringes, a pox on your endeavours.

The king of the cats is dead, dead.
Old ladies leave scraps for the scattered
hundred in alleyways.
They are building the Royal Free where he
was tyrant.
Tom is dead. I am glad he is not alive
to see what they are doing.

The King of the Cats
is Dead

Peter Porter

The light on his thigh was like
a waterfall in Iceland, and his hair
was the tidal rip between two rocks,
his claws retracted sat in softness
deeper than the ancient moss of Blarney,
his claws extended were the coulter
of the gods and a raw March wind
was in his merely agricultural yawn.
Between his back legs was a catapult
of fecundity and he was riggish
as a red-haired man. The girls
of our nation felt him brush their legs
when they were bored with telling rosaries—
at night he clawed their brains in their
coffined beds and his walnut mind
wrinkled on their scalps. His holidays
were upside down in water and then
his face was like the sun: his smell
was in the peat smoke and even his midden
was a harmony of honey. When he stalked
his momentary mice the land shook
as though Atlantic waves were bowling
at the western walls. But his eyes
were the greatest thing about him.

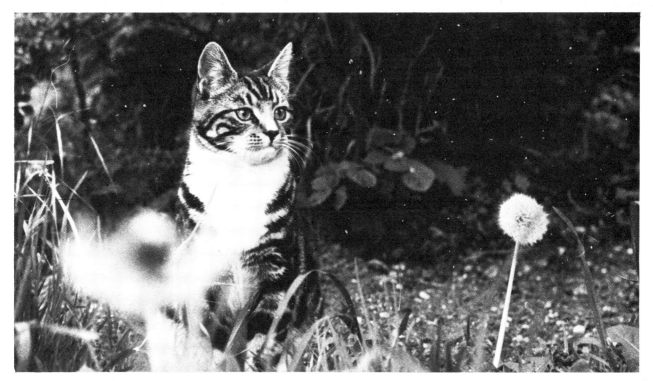

The late Fosdyke, photo Roy Deverell

They burned low and red so that drunks
saw them like two stars above a hedge,
they held the look of last eyes
in a drowning man, they were the sight
the rebel angels saw the first morning
of expulsion. And he is dead—a voice
from the centre of the earth told of his death
by treachery, that he lies in a hole
of infamy, his kidneys and his liver
torn from his body.
                                    Therefore tell
the men and horses of the marketplace,
the swallows laying twigs, the salmon
on the ladder that nothing is
as it has been
                                    time is explored
and all is known, the portents
are of brief and brutal things, since
all must hear the words of desolation,
The King of the Cats is Dead
                                    and it
is only Monday in the world.

The Age of Reason

Jean-Paul Sartre

(translated by Eric Sutton)

"Poppaea!" cried Daniel. "Poppaea, Poppaea!" Poppaea hardly ever came when called: Daniel had to go and fetch her from the kitchen. When she saw him, she jumped on to the gas stove with a sharp peevish growl. She was a stray cat, heavily scarred across her right side. Daniel had found her in the Luxembourg one winter evening, just before the garden closed, and had taken her home. She was imperious and bad-tempered, and she often bit Malvina: Daniel was fond of her. He took her in his arms, and she drew her head back, flattening her ears and arching her neck: she looked quite scandalised. He stroked her nose, and she nibbled the tip of one finger with angry playfulness: then he pinched her in the loose flesh of the neck, and she lifted a defiant little head. She did not purr—Poppaea never purred—but she looked at him, straight in the face, and Daniel thought, as indeed he often did: "A cat that looks you in the eyes is very rare." At the same time, he felt an intolerable anguish take possession of him, and had to turn his eyes away: "There, there," he said, "there, there, my beauty," and smiled at her with eyes averted. The two others had remained side by side; purring idiotically, like a grasshopper chorus. Daniel eyed them with a sort of malignant relief: "Rabbit-stew," he thought. He remembered Malvina's pink teats. It was no end of a business to get Poppaea into the basket: he had to push her in headfirst, but she turned and spat and tried to claw him. "Oh, would you now?" said Daniel. He picked her up by the neck and hindquarters, and crammed her forcibly into the basket, which creaked as Poppaea clawed it from within. Daniel took advantage of the cat's momentary stupor to slam down the lid and snap the two clasps.

"Ouf!" he ejaculated. His hand smarted slightly—with a dry little pain that was almost a tickle. He got up and eyed the basket with ironical satisfaction: safe and secure. On the back of his hand were two scratches, and in his innermost self an odd tickling sensation that promised to become unpleasant. He picked up the ball of string off the table and put it in his trouser pocket.

Then he hesitated: "It's a goodish way, I shall get pretty hot." He would have liked to wear his flannel jacket, but it was not a habit of his to yield easily to his inclinations, and besides it would be rather comical to march along in the bright sunshine, flushed and perspiring, with that burden in his arms. Comical and a trifle ridiculous: the vision made him smile and he chose his brown tweed jacket, which he had not been able to bear since the end of May. He lifted the basket by the handle, and thought; "Curse the little brutes, how heavy they are." He pictured their attitudes, humiliated and grotesque, their fury and their terror. "And that is what I was so fond of!" No sooner had he shut the three idols into a wicker basket than they became cats once more, just simply cats, small, vain, stupid mammals, stricken with panic—very far from being sacred. "Cats: merely cats." He began to laugh: he had the feeling that he was going to play an excellent trick on somebody. As he passed the flat door, his heart turned over, but the

Bagging the Cat, A. V. Venne

sensation soon passed: once on the staircase he felt hard and resolute, with an underside of strange sickliness, reminiscent of raw meat. The concierge was in her doorway, and she smiled at him. She liked Daniel because he was so ceremonious and polite.

"You are out early this morning, Monsieur Sereno."

"I was afraid you were ill, dear lady," replied Daniel with an air of concern. "I got back late last night, and I saw a light under the lodge door."

"Just imagine," said the concierge. "I was so done up that I fell asleep without turning the light off. Suddenly I heard the sound of your bell. Ah, I said to myself, there's Monsieur Sereno coming in. (You were the only tenant out.) I turned the light out immediately afterwards. I think it was about three o'clock."

"Just about . . ."

"Well," she said, "that's a large basket you've got."

"They're my cats."

"Are they ill—poor little things?"

"No, but I'm taking them to my sister's at Meudon. The vet told me they needed air." And he added gravely, "Cats tend to become tuberculous, you know."

"Tuberculous!" said the concierge, in a voice of consternation. "You must look after them carefully. All the same," she added, "they'll be missed in your flat. I had got used to seeing the little dears when I was cleaning up. You will be sorry to lose them."

"I shall indeed, Madame Dupuy," said Daniel.

He smiled at her gravely and walked on. The old mole, she gave herself away. She must have played about with them when I wasn't there; she'd much better have been attending to her daughter. Emerging from the archway he was dazzled by the light, an unpleasant, scorching, stabbing light. It hurt his eyes, which was only to be expected: when a man has been drinking the night before, a misty morning suits him best. He could no longer see anything, he was afloat in the encompassing light, with a ring of iron round his skull. Suddenly, he saw his shadow, a grotesque and stocky figure, with the shadow of the wicker basket dangling from the end of his arm. Daniel smiled: he was very tall. He drew himself to his full height, but the shadow remained squat and misshapen, like that of a chimpanzee. "Doctor Jekyll and Mr Hyde. No; I won't take a taxi," he said to himself: "I have plenty of time. I shall take Mr Hyde for an airing as far as the 72 stop." The 72 would take him to Charenton. Half a mile from there, Daniel knew a little solitary corner on the bank of the Seine. "At any rate," he said to himself, "I shan't be sick, that would be the last straw." The water of the Seine was particularly dark and dirty at that spot, being covered with greenish patches of oil from the Vitry factories. Daniel envisaged himself with disgust: he felt, within himself, so benevolent, so truly benevolent that it wasn't natural. "That," he thought, "is the real man," with a sort of satisfaction. His was a hard, forbidding character, but underneath it all was a shrinking victim pleading for mercy. It was odd, he thought, that a man could hate himself as though he were someone else. Not that that was really true: whatever he might do there was only one Daniel. When he despised himself he had the feeling of detachment from his own being, as though he were poised like an impartial judge above a noisome turmoil, then suddenly he found himself plunging downwards caught again in his own toils. "Damnation," thought he to himself. "I must get a drink." He had to make a little detour for this purpose, he would stop at Championnet's in the rue Tailledouce. When he pushed open the door, the bar was deserted. The waiter was dusting the red, wooden cask-like tables. The darkness was grateful to Daniel's eyes. "I've got a cursed headache," he thought, as he put down the basket and clambered on to one of the stools by the bar.

"A nice double whisky, I suppose," said the barman.

"No," said Daniel curtly.

"Confound these fellows' mania for classifying human beings as though they were umbrellas or sewing-machines. I am *not* so-and-so; one isn't ever anything. But they pin you down as quick as look at you. One chap gives good tips, another is always ready with a joke, and I am fond of double whiskies."

"A gin-fizz," said Daniel.

The barman served him without comment: he was no doubt offended. "So much the better," thought Daniel. He would not enter the place again, the people were too familiar. Anyway, gin-fizz tasted like a lemon-flavoured purgative. It scattered a sort of acidulated dust upon the tongue, and left a steely savour behind it. "It no longer has any effect on me," thought Daniel.

"Give me a peppered Vodka in a balloon glass."

He swallowed the Vodka and remained for a moment plunged in meditation, with a firework in his mouth. "Won't it ever end?" he thought to himself. But these were surface thoughts, as usual, cheques without funds to meet them. "What won't ever end? What won't ever end?" Whereupon a shrill miaow was heard, and the sound of scratching. The barman gave a start.

"They are cats," said Daniel curtly.

He got off the stool, flung twenty francs on to the counter and picked up the basket. As he lifted it, he noticed a tiny red drop on the floor: blood. "What can they be up to inside there," thought Daniel distressfully. But he could not bring himself to lift the lid. For the moment the little cage contained nothing but a solid, undifferentiated fear: if he opened the basket, that fear would dissolve once more into *his cats*, which Daniel could not have endured. "You couldn't endure it, eh? And supposing I did lift that lid?" But Daniel was already outside, and again the blindness fell, a clear and dewy blindness: your eyes itched, fire seemed to fill the vision, then came the sudden realisation that for moments past you have been looking at houses, houses a hundred yards ahead, airy and insubstantial, edifices of smoke. At the end of the road stood a high blue wall. "It's uncanny to see too clearly," thought Daniel. It was thus that he imagined Hell: a vision that penetrated everything, and saw to the very end of the world—the depths of a man's self. The basket shook at the extremity of his arm: the creatures inside it were clawing each other. The terror that he felt so near to his hand—Daniel wasn't sure whether it disgusted or delighted him: anyway, it came to the same thing. "There is always something to reassure them, they can smell me." And Daniel thought, "I am, indeed, for them, a smell." Patience, though: Daniel would soon be divested of that familiar smell, he would walk about without a smell, alone amid his fellow-men, who haven't fine enough senses to spot a man by his smell. Without a smell or a shadow, without a past, nothing more than an invisible uprootment from the self towards the future. Daniel noticed that he was a few steps in advance of his body— yonder, at the level of the gas-jet, and that he was watching his own progress, hobbling a little under his burden, stiff-jointed and already soaked in sweat: he saw himself come, he was no more than a disembodied vision. But the shop-window of a dyeing establishment presented his reflection, and the illusion was dispelled. Daniel filled himself with viscous, vapid water: himself: the water of the Seine, vapid and viscous, would fill the basket, and they would claw each other to pieces. A vast revulsion came upon him—this was surely a wanton act. He had stopped and set the basket on the ground. One could only damage oneself through the harm one did to others. One could never get directly at oneself. Once more he thought of Constantinople where faithless spouses were put in a sack with hydrophobic cats, and the sack thrown into the Bosphorus. Barrels, leather sacks, wicker baskets: prisons. "There are worse things." Daniel shrugged his shoulders: another thought without funds to meet it. He didn't want to adopt a tragic attitude, he had done that too often in the past. Besides, that meant taking oneself seriously. Never, never again would Daniel take himself seriously. The motor-bus suddenly appeared, Daniel waved to the driver and got into the first-class compartment.

"As far as you go."

"Six tickets," said the conductor.

Seine water would drive them crazy. Coffee-coloured water with violet gleams in it. A woman came in and sat opposite him, a prim, respectable female, with a little girl. The little girl observed the basket with interest: "Nasty little insect," thought Daniel. The basket miaowed, and Daniel started, as though he had been caught in the act of murder.

"What is it?" asked the little girl in a shrill voice.

"Hush," said her mother. "Don't annoy the gentleman."

"It's cats," said Daniel.

"Are they yours?" asked the little girl.

"Yes."

"Why are you taking them about in a basket?"

"Because they're ill," said Daniel mildly.

"May I see them?"

"Jeannine," said her mother, "mind what you're saying."

"I can't show them to you, they're ill, and rather savage."

"Oh," said the little girl in a calm, insinuating tone; "they'll be quite all right with me, the little darlings."

"Do you think so? Look here, my dear," said Daniel in a low, hurried voice, "I'm going to drown my cats, that's what I'm going to do, and do you know why? Because, no longer ago than this morning, they clawed the face of a pretty little girl like you, who came to bring me some flowers, and now she'll have to have a glass eye."

"Oh!" cried the little girl in consternation. She threw a terror-stricken glance at the basket, and clung to her mother's skirts.

"There, there," said the mother, turning indignant eyes upon Daniel. "You must keep quiet, you see, and not chatter to everyone you meet. Don't be frightened, darling, the gentleman was only joking."

Daniel returned her look placidly. "She detests me," he thought, with satisfaction. Behind the windows he could see the grey houses gliding by, and he knew that the good woman was looking at him. "An angry mother: she's looking for something to dislike in me. And it won't be my face." No one ever disliked Daniel's face. "Nor my suit, which is new and handsome. My hands perhaps." His hands were short and strong, a little fleshy, with black hairs at the joints. He spread them out on his knees ("Look at them—just look at them"). But the woman had abandoned the encounter; she was staring straight ahead of her with a crass expression on her face: she was at rest. Daniel eyed her with a kind of eagerness: these people who rested—how did they manage it? She had let her whole person sag into herself and sat dissolved in it. There was nothing in that head of hers that resembled a frantic flight from self, neither curiosity, nor hatred, nor any motion, not the faintest undulation: nothing but the thick integument of sleep. Abruptly she awoke, and an air of animation took possession of her face.

"Why, we're there," said she. "Come along! You bad little girl, you never notice anything."

She took her daughter by the hand, and dragged her off. The bus restarted and then pulled up. People passed in front of Daniel laughing.

"All change," shouted the conductor.

Daniel started: the vehicle was empty. He got up and climbed out. It was a populous square containing a number of taverns: a group of workmen and women had gathered round a hand-cart. Women eyed him with surprise. Daniel quickened his step and turned down a dirty alley that led towards the Seine. On both sides of the road there were barrels and warehouses. The basket was now miaowing incessantly, and Daniel almost ran: he was carrying a leaky bucket from which water oozed out drop by drop. Every miaow was a drop of water. The bucket was heavy, Daniel transferred it to his left hand, and wiped his forehead with his right. He must not think about the cats. Oh? So you don't want to think about the cats? Well, that's just why you *must* think of them. You can't get away with it so easily. Daniel recalled Poppaea's golden eyes, and quickly thought of whatever came first into his head—of the Bourse, where he had made ten thousand francs the day before, of Marcelle—he was going to see her that evening, it was his day: "Archangel!" Daniel grinned: he despised Marcelle profoundly. "They haven't the courage to admit that they're no longer in love. If Mathieu saw things as they were, he would have to make a decision. But he didn't want to: he didn't want to lose his bearings. He is a normal fellow," thought Daniel ironically. The cats were miaowing as though they had been scalded, and Daniel felt he would soon lose his self-control. He put the basket on the ground, and gave it a couple of violent kicks. This produced a tremendous commotion in the interior, after which the cats were silent. Daniel stood for a moment motionless, conscious of an odd shiver like a tuft behind his ears. Some workmen came out of a warehouse and Daniel resumed his journey. Here

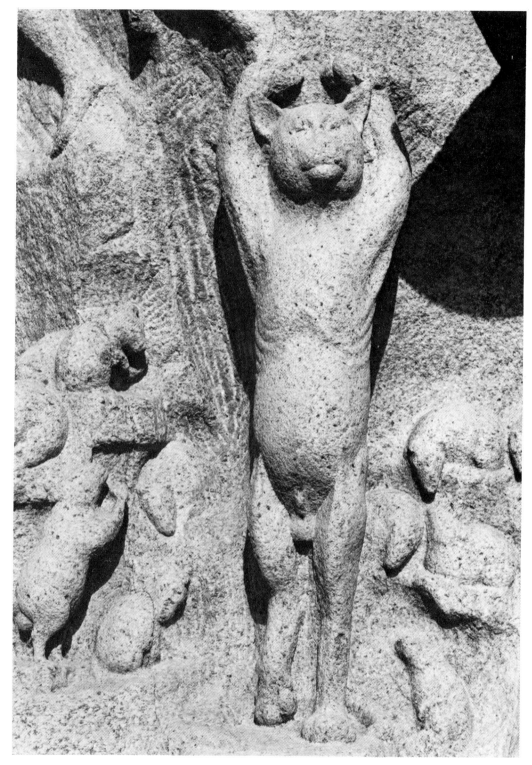

Penitent Cat at the Birth of the Ganges River, photo Paolo Koch was the place. He made his way down a stone stair to the bank of the Seine and sat down on the ground, beside an iron ring and between a barrel of tar and a heap of paving-stones. The Seine was yellow under a blue sky. Black barges loaded with casks lay moored against the opposite quay. Daniel was sitting in the sun and his temples ached. He eyed the rippling stream, swollen with patches of opal iridescence. He took the ball of string out of his pocket, and cut off a long strand with his clasp-knife: then, without getting up, and with his left hand, he picked out a paving stone. He fastened one of the ends of the string to the handle of the basket, rolled the rest of it round the stone, made several knots and replaced the stone on the ground. It looked a singular contrivance. Daniel's idea was to carry the basket in his right hand and the stone in his left hand: he would drop them into the water at the same moment. The basket would perhaps float for the tenth of a second after which it would be forcibly dragged beneath the surface and abruptly disappear. Daniel felt hot, and cursed his thick jacket, but did not want to take it off. Within him something throbbed, something pleaded for mercy, and Daniel, the hard and resolute Daniel, heard himself say in mournful tones: "When a man hasn't the courage to kill himself wholesale, he must do so retail." He would walk down to the water and say: "Farewell to what I love most in the world . . ." He raised himself slightly on his hands and looked about him: on his right the bank was deserted, on his left—some distance away, he could see a fisherman, a black figure in the sunshine. The ripples would spread *under water* to the cork on the man's line. "He'll think he's had a bite." Daniel laughed and pulled out his handkerchief to wipe away the sweat that beaded his forehead. The hands of his wrist-watch stood at eleven twenty-five. "At half-past eleven!" He must prolong that strange moment: Daniel had split into two entities; he felt himself *lost* in a scarlet cloud, under a leaden sky. He thought of Mathieu with a sort of pride. "It is *I* who am free," he said to himself. But it was an impersonal pride, for Daniel was no longer a person. At eleven twenty-nine he got up and felt so weak that he had to lean against the barrel. He got a smear of tar on to his tweed jacket, and looked at it.

He saw the black smear on the brown material, and suddenly he felt that he was one person and no more. One only. A coward. A man who liked his cats and could not chuck them in the river. He picked up his pocket-knife, bent down, and cut the string. In silence. Even within himself there was silence now, he was too ashamed to talk in his own presence. He picked up the basket again, and climbed the stair: it was as though he were walking with averted head past someone who regarded him with contempt. Within himself desolation and silence still reigned. When he reached the top of the steps he ventured to speak his first words to himself: "What was that drop of blood?" But he didn't dare open the basket: he walked on, limping as he went. It is I: it is I: it is I. The evil thing. But in the depths of him there was an odd little smile because he had saved Poppaea.

"Taxi!" he shouted.

IX

Cat's Resurrection

Extract from the Will of Miss Topping, who died in Vendôme, May 1841

I desire that there shall be raised from the most easily convertible part of my property a capital sum sufficient to produce 800 f. a year, which shall be paid quarterly to such person as I may name . . . on condition of taking the care and nourishment of my three favourite cats, Nina, Fanfan and Mini . . . The person [so] appointed shall live on a groundfloor, to which shall adjoin a terrace easy of access and a garden enclosed within walls, of which they shall have full and free enjoyment . . . They are to sleep in the house, and therefore are to be shut up after their supper.

The Times, March 1843

Three Cats, Benjamin Cam Norton (*Michael Parkin Fine Art Ltd*)

Car Fights Cat

Alan Sillitoe

In a London crescent curving vast
A cat sat—
Between two rows of molar houses
With birdsky in each grinning gap.

Cat small—coal and snow
Road wide—a zone of tar set hard and fast
With four-wheeled speedboats cutting
A dash
    for it from
              time to time.

King Cat walked warily midstream
As if silence were no warning on this silent road
Where even a man would certainly have crossed
With hands in pockets and been whistling.

The cat heard it, but royalty and indolence
Weighed its paws to hobnailed boots
Held it from the dragons-teeth of safety first and last,
Until some Daimler hurrying from work
Caused cat to stop and wonder where it came from—
Instead of zig-zag scattering to hide itself.

Maybe a deaf malevolence descended
And cat thought car would pass in front—
So spun and walked all fur and confidence
Into the dreadful tyre-treads . . . . .
A wheel caught hold of it and
FEARSOME THUDS
Sounded from the night-time of black axles in
UNEQUAL FIGHT
That stopped the heart to hear it.

But cat shot out with limbs still solid,
Bolted—spitting fire and gravel
At unjust God who built such massive
Catproof motorcars in his graven image,
Its mind made up to lose and therefore win
By winging towards
The wisdom toothgaps of the canyon houses
LEGS AND BRAIN INTACT.

Let No Man Put Asunder

Graham Fawcett

The road ran straight for the first mile, as far as the signpost. The white arms pointed black letters to the Church and the Mouth. The Church road coiled its way under the shadow of high hedges and then out into sunlight, stretching beyond the graveyard and the Saxon tower to pitch forward easing to a slope down several hundred yards to the bridge.

Here the two rivers became one: Torridge from the Northern moor, Bere from the valley to the West. Priestlike the old bridge received their union, an altargate to the ordination of water by water seconds before its unmaking. Higher than the bridge and astride the narrowing land between the currents stood the Mill, where the man and the woman lived and nearly a century had passed since the last turning of the wheels.

For this Mill had two wheels: quite independent, they waited only on the mood or season of water from moor or valley. And yet it was said that when one had turned, the other had stood still—no sound from its shackchamber but the simple sameness of shallow water trickling beneath the silent wheel and on towards the bridge.

When the man and the woman had come to the house, they had found a cat which already belonged there. She'd been called Mouthwatch because she would sit every day on the parapet of the bridge below the Mill and watch the two rivers joining together and stumbling down to the Mouth and the open sea. Mouthwatch had led them everywhere from that first day: through the high wooden gates, along the short drive which forked to avoid trees and stopped before the orchard. Then into the kitchen garden and over the fence to the meadow surrounded by steep wooded banks. At the far end of the meadow the trees closed in and the only path—the cat went slowly here—crossed the shallower Torridge on large smooth stones before drifting along cart tracks and disappearing suddenly through a gap in the low rock wall which marked the boundary between Mill land and the lost world on the other side of the trees. That wall—and Mouthwatch would never cross it—ran cleanly along a line of massive elms into a wild climb of struggling branches and no eventual light.

The night that Mouthwatch was due to give birth there was a gale and rain. Mouthwatch left the house in search of shelter. Towards midnight, they took lanterns and went outside to listen in the dark and the steady rain for sound of her. They looked in all the usual places, stood and held their breath in the night and heard nothing. Then as they turned to go inside, they stopped. Below the house from the direction of the bridge there was a single cry. Then silence. They headed towards the noise, its echo already deadened by the rain. The sound of running water increased as they came out on to the road that led to the bridge. The rain fell harder, and, in the light of the lantern, straighter. There was no more noise. They saw nothing.

The next morning the rain had stopped and the sky was light with cloud. After breakfast they went out and took the same path as the night before. When they reached the bridge, they stopped to rest and leaned on the parapet looking towards the Mouth and the falling, single river. If they had not then looked directly down, they might never have noticed Mouthwatch half-hidden from sight and lying on the narrow bank beneath the bridge. They climbed down to look closer. She was alive, clearly, and so were her clinging young. It was not until the man took a small twig and stirred them gently that he realised: the kittens were clinging not only to her but to each other. They were joined together at the side.

Mouthwatch would not let them touch her or the litter. The man and the woman could only turn away and walk back along the road towards the high wooden gates of the house. At the end of the drive they continued across the orchard and into the meadow, past the disused caravan and the corn elevator haunched on its large iron wheels in the tall grass. Through the gap in the trees they could see as they drew nearer that the wind had brought down branches which had dammed Torridge's flatstone crossing. The man reflected: if that had not happened, the river would have been higher, much higher at the bridge and the cats could not have survived the height and power of the double rush of water. He walked down into the water and made to begin to clear the fallen branches. Then he stopped. They were still there, under the bridge. The water was lower now but the stream must stay blocked until they could be moved.

The rain came back the next night, harder than before. The woman pleaded that they should go to the cats and try to bring them home, however difficult it might be and at whatever risk of injury to them. It was already dark when the man went out to get them. At the top of the steps leading down from the door he stumbled and fell. The lantern smashed on the stone and the smell of warm paraffin mixed with that of wet grass. Picking himself up, he turned back inside the house for the keys to the caravan in the meadow. There was an old lantern in there—he had to get it—which had not been used for a long time. He hurried through the kitchen garden, climbed the rough wood fence and ran on into the meadow. He had just reached the caravan and felt the lock take the key when he heard a creaking and then a rushing of water. The dam had given way and the river, swollen by new rain, was already racing down the course towards the bridge. It would be too late. He was stepping out of the caravan with the lit lantern in his hand before he heard another, quite different sound. As he hurried back towards the house and passed the shackchamber of the Torridge wheel, he knew. With the onrush of the flood the wheel had begun to turn. He ran back across the orchard, out into the road and down to the bridge. He leaned straining over the parapet and held the lantern down as far as he could reach in the direction of Mouthwatch's hiding place. There was nothing; and as he watched he saw the water rising as it washed the bank.

When day came, the urgency of the darkness had gone. Neither of them wanted to go outside. But as the sun came out and the air grew warmer, the woman opened the window and looked out across the orchard. She was looking at the chamber of the Torridge wheel and the man saw her. Together they went out to see for themselves what signs there might be that it had turned in the storm. It lay, still again, in the breathing sunlight, with no trace of sudden life.

But there was something else. In the deep well of the wheel was a small black separate kitten. Across the stone pathway, in the well of the Bere stream wheel, lay the other. Each bore a patch of white skin on one side. And as the man and the woman watched, so did a third cat—sitting on the parapet of the bridge below the Mill watching the two rivers become one on their way to the Mouth and the open sea.

Newborn Kitten, photo Will Green

To A Slow Drum

George MacBeth

I
Solitary thoughts,
and burial mounds,
begin this dirge,
and mournful sounds.

II
Now to the dead march
troop in twos,
the granite owls
with their *Who Was Who's*,
the bat, and the grave, yew
bear on his wheels,
Tuborg the pig
with his hard wood heels.

[271]

III

Gemmed with a dew
of morning tears,
    the weeping armadillo
has brought his shears:
    the droop-ear dog
and the lion come,
    dipping their long waists
to meet the drum.

IV

On the bare chafing-dish
as each one hears,
    the grey lead pigs
reverse their spears:
    grooved in line,
they show no grief,
    grouped above a sere
and yellow leaf,
    a tree's life blown
through a crack in the door.

V

Over the red-black
kitchen floor,
    Jeremy the spider
stalks to his place,
    all eight legs
wet from the waste:
    he climbed up the drain
to be here on time.

VI

Now, to the slow
egg-timer's chime,
    shiny in state
come things from the grime:
    tiny slaters
with wings and hoods,
    beetles from the closet
under the stairs:
    gashed with sorrow
each fixed eye stares.

Creation of the Animals, Paul Brill (*Galleria Doria, Rome*)

VII
Fairbanks crawls
from his winter leaves:
    he rubs his eyes
on his prickling sleeves:
    rattling his plate
for a sad sound,
    his black legs cover
the chill ground
    at a fair speed:
he creeps to our need.

[273]

VIII

Now the hall resounds
to the tread of toes
      as each one gathers,
and the crowd grows:
      broken-spirited,
the bears upstairs
      troop to the banisters
and droop their ears:
      the brown one squats,
glum cheeks in his paws,
      the blue one strums
a melancholy string.

IX

From all feasts of fish
he wove good fur:
      alas, no fish
stale death can deter.

The Garden of Delights (detail), Hieronymus Bosch (*Museo del Prado, Madrid*)

X

        As the drum beats,
the long cortège
        winds to the attic
as towards the stage:
        some hop and skip,
some crawl or run,
        the sad music
holds every one:
        crouched by the window
all weep to view
        Peter, poor Peter,
drift up the flue.

XI

        Now, all together
they chant his dirge,
        grouped by the ledge
where the chimneys merge.

XII

        Peter, salt Peter,
fish-eating cat,
        feared by the blackbird,
stung by the gnat,
        wooden-spider collector,
lean as a rat,
        soon you shall fall
to a fine grey fat.

XIII

        Peter, salt Peter,
drift into the wind,
        enter the water
where all have sinned:
        forgive us our trespasses
as we forgive yours:
        remember us in heaven
as clean scales and furs,
        as we you on earth here
when any cat purrs.

XIV

        Peter, salt Peter,
farewell and live,
        as we do remembering
and so forgive.

XV
Over the whole world
a sad pall falls,
        fur into fine air,
bone into ash:
        a chill water
wets every lash.

XVI
Peter, salt Peter,
by pleurisy slain,
        the pale glass weeps
in its wooden pane,
        come to the cat-flap
and slap in again.

XVII
Peter, salt Peter,
the bird of death,
        a boding raven
chokes off my breath.

XVIII
Wrung warm tears,
and doleful words
        end this dirge,
and the screams of birds.

Pets

Ted Hughes

A dark November night. Late. The back door wide.
Beyond the doorway, the step off into space.
On the threshold, looking out,
With foxy furry tail lifted, a kitten.
Somewhere out there a badger, our lodger,
A stripe-faced rusher at cats, a grim savager,
Is crunching the bones and meat of a hare

That I left out for her twilight emergence
From under the outhouses.
The kitten flirts its tail, arches its back,
All its hairs are inquisitive.
Dare I go for a pee?
Something is moving there—just in dark.
A prowling lump. A tabby Tom. Grows.
And the battered master of the house
After a month at sea, comes through the doorway,
Recovered from his nearly fatal mauling,
Two probably three pounds heavier
Since that last appearance
When he brought in his remains to die or be doctored.
He deigns to recognise me,
With his criminal eyes, his deformed voice.
Then poises, head lowered, muscle-bound,
Like a bull for the judges,
A thick Devon bull,
Sniffing the celebration of sardines.

Gunner

Martin Booth

Dropped in a cannon's maw
upon the "Victory"
grandfather named him *Gunner*
out of fact and quandary
disliking *Drake* or *Nelson*

through Essex and life's countryside
he bore himself with dignity
in glory or defeat
or astride a seasoning queen
under the gooseberry bushes
when I was five

Gunner, photo Martin Booth

now just a fading sepia plate
in childhood's album
he haunts my dreams
re-lives his scars and killings
while I sleep
and has his paw pressed firmly to my pulse

over the twenty years
since his death
(guardian of my grandmother's fire-tongs)
he has kept re-occurring
as king cat
feles universalis
the harbinger of good tidings in early hours
—warned me of my marriage
and scorns my adult love of dogs

today
for the first time
I've bought a home he'd like:
cornfields
an old church
oblivious thrushes tugging at the lawn

even my dog *Chester*
ageing
would bow and let dead *Gunner* by

under the ripe apples
he suns and squints at distance:
under the gooseberries
his echo is shrieking for a mate

The Cat as Cat

Denise Levertov

The cat on my bosom
sleeping and purring
—fur-petalled chrysanthemum,
squirrel-killer—

is a metaphor only if I
force him to be one,
looking too long in his pale, fond,
dilating, contracting eyes

that reject mirrors, refuse
to observe what bides
stockstill.
      Likewise

flex and reflex of claws
gently pricking through sweater to skin
gently sustains their own tune,
not mine. I-Thou, cat, I-Thou.

Child with Cat, François Drouais (*Musée Cognacq-Jay, Paris*)

Epitaph on the Duchess
of Maine's Cat

La Mothe le Vayer
(translated by Sir Edmund Gosse)

Puss passer-by, within this simple tomb
Lies one whose life fell Atropos hath shred;
The happiest cat on earth hath heard her doom,
And sleeps for ever in a marble bed.
Alas! what long delicious days I've seen!
O cats of Egypt, my illustrious sires,
You who on altars, bound with garlands green,
Have melted hearts, and kindled fond desires,
Hymns in your praise were paid, and offerings too,
But I'm no*t* jealous of those rights divine,
Since Ludovisa loved me, close and true,
Your ancient glory was less proud than mine.
To live a simple pussy by her side
Was nobler far than to be deified.

Index of Authors

Index of Artists

Text Acknowledgments

The publishers gratefully acknowledge the permission of the following to reprint the copyright material in this book:

Paul Ableman: *Aunty and Her Cats*, the author.

Alan Brownjohn: *Cat* from *Brownjohn's Beasts*, Macmillan of London and Basingstoke; *The Seventh Knight and the Green Cat*, the author.

Jeni Couzyn: *The King of the Cats is Dead* from *Monkeys' Wedding*, Jonathan Cape Ltd.

Walter de la Mare: *Broomsticks* and *Five Eyes*, The Literary Trustees of Walter de la Mare, and the Society of Authors as their representative.

Richard Eberhart: *Old Tom* from *Collected Poems 1930–1976*, Copyright © by Richard Eberhart 1960, 1976. Chatto & Windus and Oxford University Press, Inc.

T. S. Eliot: *Growltiger's Last Stand* and *Macavity* from *Old Possum's Book of Practical Cats*, Copyright, 1939, by T. S. Eliot; copyright, 1967, by Esme Valerie Eliot. Faber and Faber Ltd, and Harcourt Brace Jovanovich, Inc.

Graham Fawcett: *Let No Man Put Asunder*, the author.

Roy Fuller: *Cat and Fiddle*, the author; *The Family Cat* and *In Memory of My Cat Domino*, Andre Deutsch Ltd.

Paul Gallico: *The Ballad of Tough Tom* from *Honourable Cat* published by William Heinemann Ltd and Crown Publishers, Inc; *"When in Doubt—Wash"* from *The Abandoned* Copyright 1950, published by William Heinemann Ltd and Alfred A. Knopf, Inc; by permission of Hughes Massie Ltd and Harold Ober Associates Inc.

Giles Gordon: *The Jealous One*, the author.

Robert Graves: *Cat-Goddesses* from *Collected Poems 1965*, the author.

Michael Hamburger: *Cat* from *Travelling* published by Fulcrum Press, the author.

Thomas Hardy: *Last Words to a Dumb Friend* from *Collected Poems of Thomas Hardy*, Copyright 1925 by Macmillan Publishing Co, Inc. The Trustees of the Hardy Estate, Macmillan of London and Basingstoke, Macmillan Company of Canada Limited, Macmillan Publishing Co, Inc.

Patricia Highsmith; *Ming's Biggest Prey*, the author.

Geoffrey Holloway: *On Clem*, the author and London Magazine Editions.

Ted Hughes: *Esther's Tomcat* from *Lupercal*, Faber and Faber Ltd and Harper & Row, Publishers; *How the Cat Became* from *How the Whale Became*, Faber and Faber Ltd and Atheneum Publishers; *Pets*, the author.

Aldous Huxley: *Sermons in Cats* from *Collected Essays*, Bantam Books, Inc.

Harvey Jacobs: *What Did You Do There?*, the author.

W. W. Jacobs: *The White Cat*, the Society of Authors as the literary representatives of the Estate of W. W. Jacobs.

Rudyard Kipling: *The Cat that Walked by Himself* from *The Just So Stories*, the late Mrs George Bambridge, the Macmillan Company of London and Basingstoke, Doubleday & Co, Inc.

Robert Leach: *Dostoievsky* from *Cats Free & Familiar* published by The Keepsake Press, the author.

Denise Levertov: *The Cat as Cat* from *The Sorrow Dance*, Copyright © 1966 by Denise Levertov. Jonathan Cape Ltd and New Directions Publishing Corporation.

Illustration Acknowledgments

In addition to the owners named under the illustrations, the following sources must be acknowledged most gratefully by the publishers: John Bignell, 82, 112; John Blackwell, 257; Mary Evans Picture Library, 11, 23, 24, 31, 34, 39, 45, 62, 90, 167, 221; Photographie Giraudon, 20, 41, 65, 81, 101, 133, 152, 163, 176, 178, 180, 201, 204, 212, 230, 242; Mansell Collection, 124, 126, 128, 130, 135, 174, 189, 194, 218, 234, 255, 259, 273, 280; Eileen Tweedy, colour plates by Jillian Peccinotti, Sheila Robinson, Louis Wain, and of *Lady Chasing Cat with Parrot* and *Cat with a Fish in its Mouth*; John Webb, colour plate by David Hockney.

The following copyright owners must also be thanked for their permission to reproduce: ADAGP, 120, 180; William Heinemann Ltd, 75 (from *Honourable Cat*); Office du Livre, Fribourg, 139; Portal Gallery, colour plate by James Lloyd; SPADEM, 101, 133; Frederick Warne & Co Ltd, 161, 196 (from *The Tailor of Gloucester*).